easy Guitar

Chart Toppers

14.95

Wise Publications
London/New York/Paris/Sydney/Copenhagen/Madrid

14.95

Exclusive Distributors:
Music Sales Limited
8-9 Frith Street,
London W1V 5TZ, England.
Music Sales Pty Limited
120 Rothschild Avenue,
Rosebery, NSW 2018,
Australia.

Order No. AM951930
ISBN 0-7119-7280-X
This book © Copyright 1999 by Wise Publications

Compiled by Peter Evans
Music arranged by Rob Smith
Music processed by Andrew Shiels
Cover design by Studio Twenty, London
Cover photography by Julian Hawkins
Printed in the United Kingdom by
Redwood Books, Trowbridge

Your Guarantee of Quality
As publishers, we strive to produce every book to the
highest commercial standards.
The music has been freshly engraved and the book
has been carefully designed to minimise awkward
page turns and to make playing from it a real
pleasure.
Particular care has been given to specifying acid-
free, neutral-sized paper made from pulps which
have not been elemental chlorine bleached. This
pulp is from farmed sustainable forests and was
produced with special regard for the environment.
Throughout, the printing and binding have been
planned to ensure a sturdy, attractive publication
which should give years of enjoyment.
If your copy fails to meet our high standards,
please inform us and we will gladly replace it.

Music Sales' complete catalogue describes
thousands of titles and is available in full colour
sections by subject, direct from Music Sales Limited.
Please state your areas of interest and send a
cheque/postal order for £1.50 for postage to:
Music Sales Limited, Newmarket Road,
Bury St. Edmunds, Suffolk IP33 3YB.

www.internetmusicshop.com

Other titles in the
Easy Guitar series...
Classic Hits
Order No. AM951940

Top Pops
Order No. AM951962

All-Time Hits
Order No. AM951951

After The Goldrush *Neil Young* 4

All Right Now *Free* 6

All You Need Is Love *The Beatles* 18

America *Simon & Garfunkel* 8

Barbie Girl *Aqua* 10

Big Yellow Taxi *Joni Mitchell* 14

Blue Suede Shoes *Elvis Presley* 16

Call Me *Blondie* 21

Careless Whisper *George Michael* 24

Cecilia *Simon & Garfunkel* 26

Common People *Pulp* 28

D'You Know What I Mean? *Oasis* 33

Dancing Queen *Abba* 36

Daniel *Elton John* 41

Don't You (Forget About Me) *Simple Minds* 44

Ebony and Ivory *Paul McCartney with Stevie Wonder* 50

Eight Days A Week *The Beatles* 52

Every Breath You Take *The Police* 47

Everybody (Backstreet's Back) *Backstreet Boys* 56

Everyday *Buddy Holly* 54

(Everything I Do) I Do It For You *Bryan Adams* 59

Girls And Boys *Blur* 64

Good Vibrations *The Beach Boys* 62

Hanging On The Telephone *Blondie* 67

Heartbeat *Buddy Holly* 70

Hotel California *The Eagles* 72

I Shall Be Released *Bob Dylan* 76

I Shot The Sheriff *Bob Marley* 78

In The Air Tonight *Phil Collins* 92

Ironic *Alanis Morissette* 80

Jamming *Bob Marley* 84

Jealous Guy *John Lennon* 86

Just Like A Woman *Bob Dylan* 88

Lyin' Eyes *The Eagles* 90

Money For Nothing *Dire Straits* 95

No More Heroes *The Stranglers* 98

Norwegian Wood *The Beatles* 104

One More Night *Phil Collins* 100

Paperback Writer *The Beatles* 105

Pinball Wizard *The Who* 108

Private Investigations *Dire Straits* 112

Proud Mary *Creedence Clearwater Revival* 110

Remember How We Started *Paul Weller* 115

Sailing *Rod Stewart* 118

Saturday Night *Suede* 124

She Bangs The Drums *The Stone Roses* 120

Stayin' Alive *The Bee Gees* 127

Still Crazy After All These Years *Paul Simon* 130

Tears In Heaven *Eric Clapton* 132

The Day We Caught The Train
Ocean Colour Scene 134

The Riverboat Song *Ocean Colour Scene* 137

Tupelo Honey *Van Morrison* 140

Walking On The Moon *The Police* 144

Waterloo Sunset *The Kinks* 146

Where The Streets Have No Name *U2* 141

Wonderwall *Oasis* 150

Words *Boyzone/The Bee Gees* 148

Yesterday *The Beatles* 153

You Oughta Know *Alanis Morissette* 158

Your Song *Elton John* 154

Zombie *The Cranberries* 156

After The Gold Rush

Words & Music by Neil Young

Well, I dreamed I saw the knights in ar - mour com - in', say - in'

(Verses 2&3 see block lyric)

some - thing a - bout a queen. There were peas - ants sing - in' and

drum - mers drum - min' and the arch - er split the tree. There was a

fan - fare blow - in' to the sun that was float - ing on the breeze.

Look at Moth - er Na - ture on the run in the

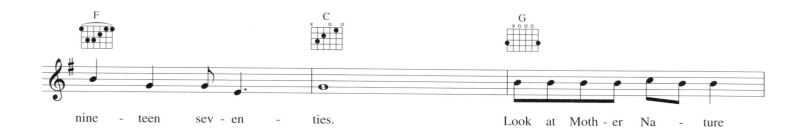

nine - teen sev - en - ties. Look at Moth - er Na - ture

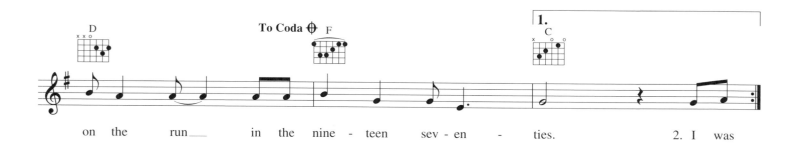

on the run___ in the nine - teen sev - en - ties. 2. I was

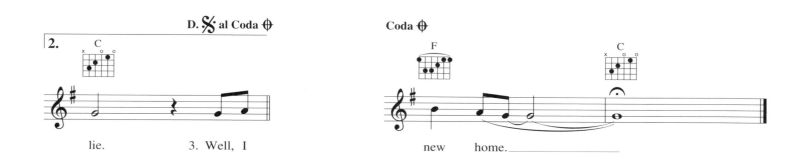

lie. 3. Well, I

new home.___

Verse 2:   I was lyin' in a burned out basement with the full moon in my eyes
I was hopin' for a replacement when the sun burst through the sky
There was a band playin' in my head and I felt like getting high
I was thinkin' about what a friend had said, I was hopin' it was a lie
Thinkin' about what a friend had said, I was hopin' it was a lie.

Verse 3:   Well, I dreamed I saw the silver spaceships flyin' in the yellow haze of the sun
There were children cryin' and colours flyin' all around the chosen ones
All in a dream, all in a dream, the loading had begun
Flying Mother Nature's silver seed to a new home in the sun
Flying Mother Nature's silver seed to a new home.

All Right Now

Words & Music by Paul Rodgers & Andy Fraser

America

Words & Music by Paul Simon

Intro

Capo 3rd fret

Mm   Mm   Mm   Mm

* Symbols in parentheses represent chord names with respect to capoed guitar
Symbols above reflect actual sounding chords

"Let us be lov-ers, we'll marr-y our for-tunes to-ge-ther._____ I've got some

(Verse 2 see block lyric)

real es-tate here in my bag."_____ So we bought a pack of ci-ga-rettes,_____ and

Mrs___ Wag-ner's pies,_____ and walked off____ to look for A-me-ri-ca.____

"Ka-thy," I said, as we board-ed a Grey-hound in

Pitts-burgh,_____ "Mi-chi-gan seems like a dream to me now.

8

Lyrics with the melody:

It took me four days to hitch-hike from Sa-gi-naw. I've come___ to look for A-me-ri-ca."___

Laugh-ing on the bus,___ play-ing games with the fa-ces,___ she said the man in the ga-bar-dine suit was a spy.___ I said "Be care-ful, his bow-tie is real-ly a cam-'ra."___

To Coda ⊕

D. % al Coda ⊕

Coda ⊕

All come___ to look for A-me-ri-ca.___

Repeat to fade

Verse 2:   "Toss me a cigarette, I think there's one in my raincoat"
"We smoked the last one an hour ago"
So I looked at the scenery
She read her magazine
And the moon rose over an open field
"Kathy I'm lost" I said, though I knew she was sleeping
"I'm empty and aching and I don't know why"
Counting the cars on the New Jersey turnpike
They've all come to look for America.

Barbie Girl

Words & Music by Soren Rasted, Claus Norreen, Rene Dif, Lene Nystrom, Johnny Pederson & Karsten Delgado

Come on Bar - bie, let's go par - ty. Ooh,_____ ooh._____ I'm a Bar - bie girl

in a Bar - bie world,_____ life in plas - tic, it's fan - tas - tic.

You can brush my hair, un - dress me ev - 'ry - where_____ i - ma - gi - na - tion,

life is your cre - a - tion,____ Come on Bar - bie, let's go par - ty. Ah ah ah yeah.___

Come on Bar - bie, let's go par - ty. Ooh,_____ ooh._____ Come on Bar - bie, let's go par - ty.

Ah ah ah yeah.___ Come on Bar - bie, let's go par - ty. Ooh,_____ ooh._____

Spoken: Ooh, I'm having so much fun Barbie. We're just getting started. Ooh, I love you Ken!

Big Yellow Taxi

Words & Music by Joni Mitchell

Moderate Rock beat

Strum pattern

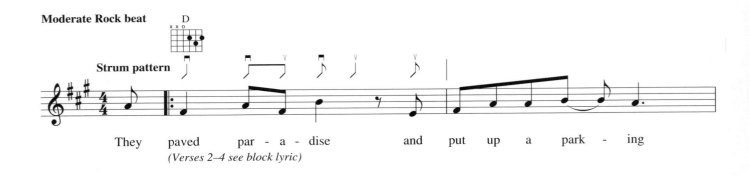

They paved par - a - dise and put up a park - ing
(Verses 2–4 see block lyric)

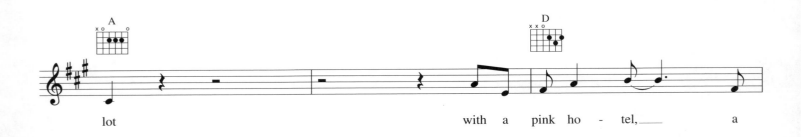

lot with a pink ho - tel,___ a

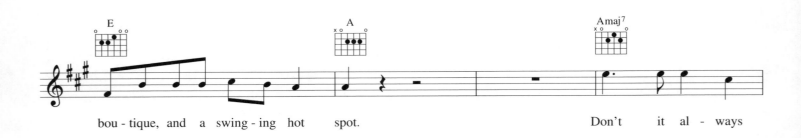

bou - tique, and a swing - ing hot spot. Don't it al - ways

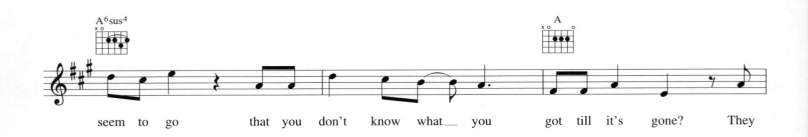

seem to go that you don't know what___ you got till it's gone? They

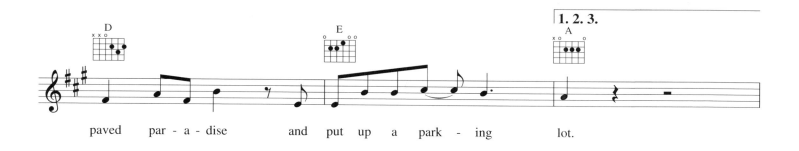

paved   par - a - dise   and   put   up   a   park - ing   lot.

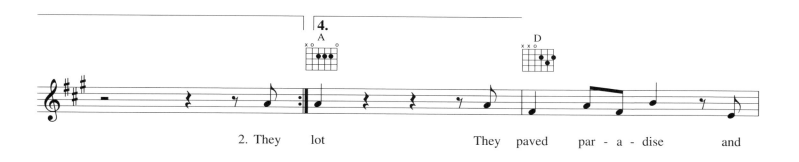

2. They   lot   They   paved   par - a - dise   and

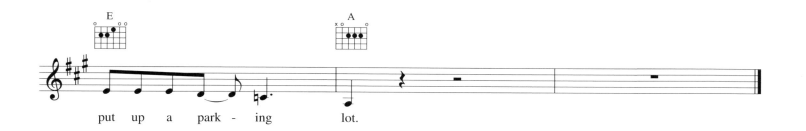

put   up   a   park - ing   lot.

Verse 2   They took all the trees and put them in a tree museum
And they charged all the people a dollar and a half just to see 'em
Don't it always seem to go that you don't know what you've got till it's gone?
They paved paradise and put up a parking lot.

Verse 3   Hey, farmer, farmer, put away that D.D.T. now
Give me spots on my apples but leave me the birds and the bees, please!
Don't it always seem to go that you don't know what you've got till it's gone?
They paved paradise and put up a parking lot.

Verse 4   Late last night I heard the screen door slam
And a big yellow taxi took away my old man
Don't it always seem to go that you don't know what you've got till it's gone?
They paved paradise and put up a parking lot
They paved paradise and put up a parking lot.

Blue Suede Shoes

Words & Music by Carl Lee Perkins

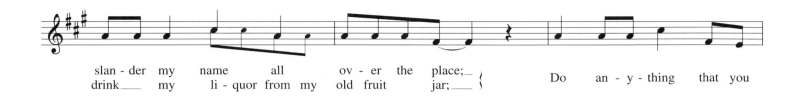

slan - der my name all ov - er the place;
drink my li - quor from my old fruit jar;

Do an - y - thing that you

want to do,___ but uh - uh, ho - ney lay off of my shoes.___

Chorus

D7   A

Strum pattern 2

Don't you step on my blue suede shoes.

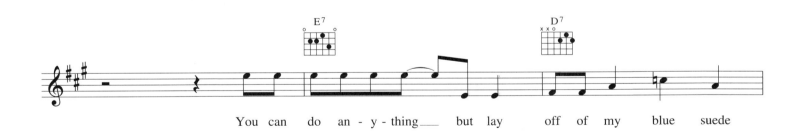

E7   D7

You can do an - y - thing___ but lay off of my blue suede

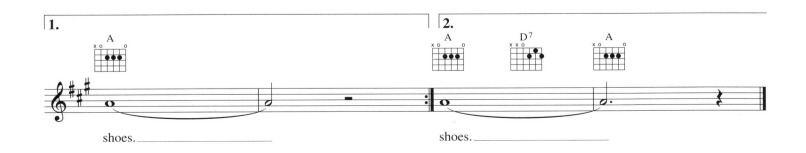

1.

A

shoes.___

2.

A   D7   A

shoes.___

All You Need Is Love

Words & Music by John Lennon & Paul McCartney

Intro
Moderately ♩ = 98

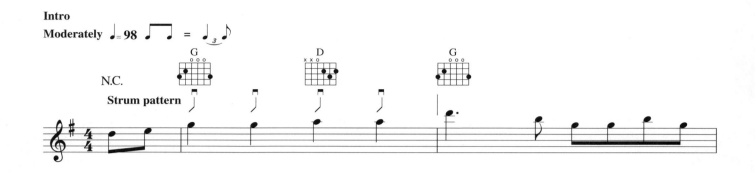

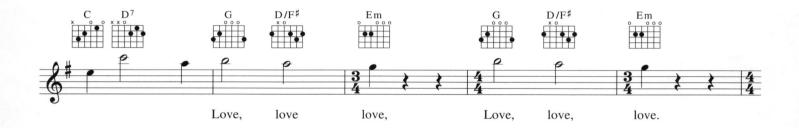

Love,   love   love,   Love,   love,   love.

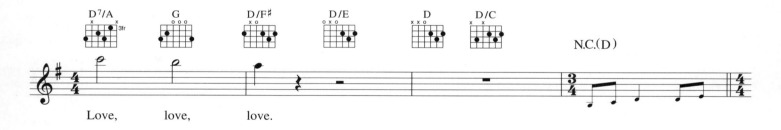

Love,   love,   love.

Verse

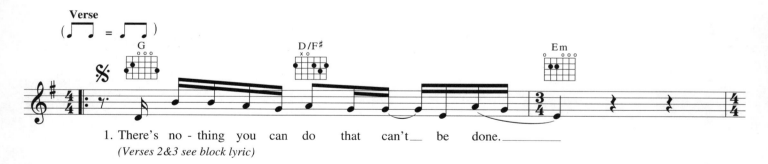

1. There's no-thing you can do that can't be done.
(Verses 2&3 see block lyric)

Noth-ing you can sing that can't be sung.

Noth - ing you can say, but you can learn how to play the game. It's

Chorus

ea - sy.   All you need is love____

All you need is love.____   All you need is love,____ love.____

Guitar Solo

Love is all___ you need.___   Love, love, love.

Love, love, love.   Love, love, love.

Chorus

All you need is love.____   All you need is love.____

19

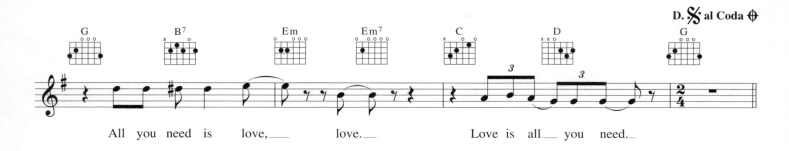

All you need is love,___ love.___ Love is all___ you need.___

Coda ⊕

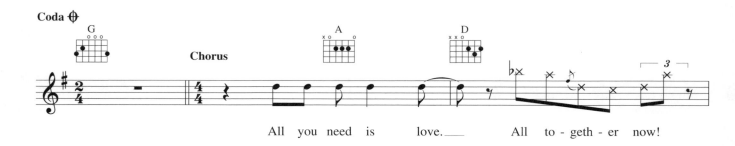

Chorus

All you need is love.___ All to - geth - er now!

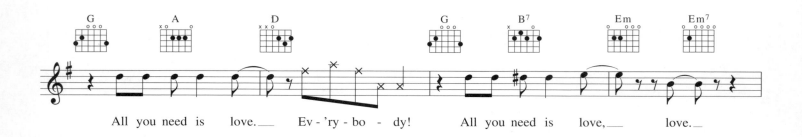

All you need is love.___ Ev - 'ry - bo - dy! All you need is love,___ love.__

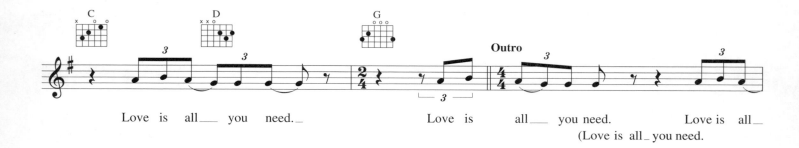

Outro

Love is all___ you need.__ Love is all___ you need. Love is all__

(Love is all_ you need.

Play 12 times and fade

___ you need.__ Love is all___ you need.__ Love is all you need.__ Love is all___
Love is all_ you need.) (Love is all_ you need. Love is all_ you need.)

Verse 2   Nothing you can make that can't be made
           No one you can save that can't be saved
           Nothing you can do but you can learn how to be you in time
           It's easy.

Verse 3   There's nothing you can know that isn't known
           Nothing you can see that isn't shown
           There's nowhere you can be that isn't where you're meant to be
           It's easy.

Call Me

Words & Music by Deborah Harry & Giorgio Moroder

Careless Whisper

Words & Music by George Michael & Andrew Ridgeley

Intro

Strum pattern

Verse

1. I feel so___ un - sure
2. Time can nev - er mend___
(Verse 3 see block lyric)

___ as I take your hand___ and lead you to the dance floor:
___ the care - less whis - per of a good friend;

as the mu - sic dies___ some - thing in your eyes___
to the heart and mind___ ig - no - rance is kind___

calls to mind a sil - ver screen___ and you're its sad good - bye.
there's no com - fort in the truth___ pain is all you'll find.

Verse 3:

Tonight the music seems so loud
I wish that we could lose this crowd
Maybe it's better this way
If we'd hurt each other with the things we want to say
We could have been so good together
We could have lived this dance forever
But now who's gonna dance with me?
Please dance.

Cecilia

Words & Music by Paul Simon

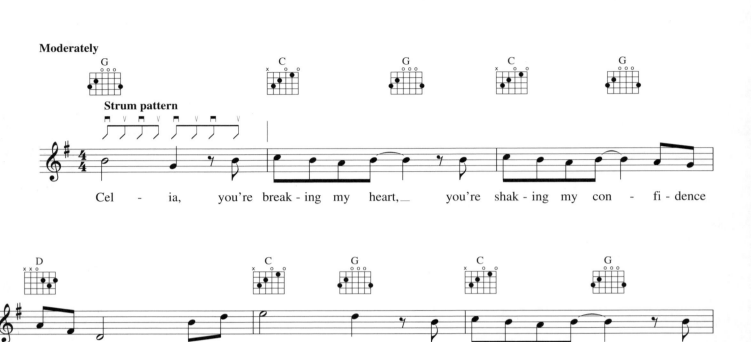

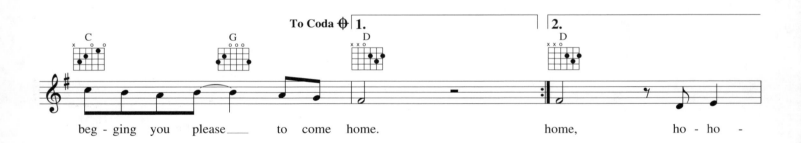

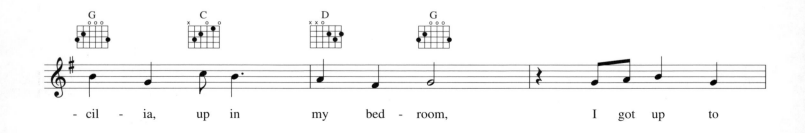

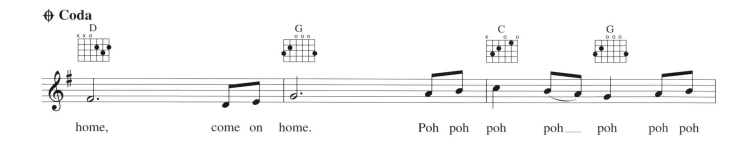

wash my face when I come back to bed,___ some-one's ta-ken my place.___

✛ **Coda**

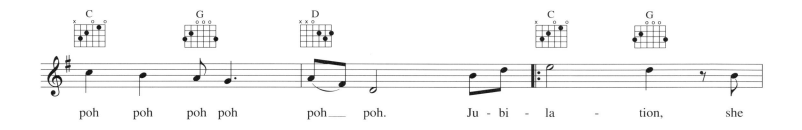

home, come on home. Poh poh poh poh___ poh poh poh

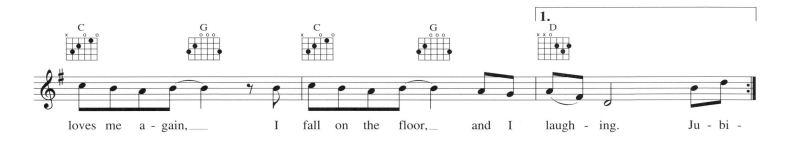

poh poh poh poh poh___ poh. Ju-bi-la - tion, she

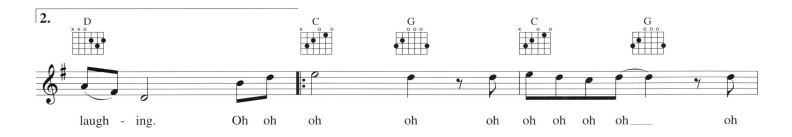

loves me a-gain,___ I fall on the floor,___ and I laugh-ing. Ju-bi -

laugh - ing. Oh oh oh oh oh oh oh oh oh___ oh

oh oh oh oh___ oh oh oh oh. Oh oh oh oh, come on home.

Common People

Music by Pulp. Lyrics by Jarvis Cocker

Intro

Strum pattern

Verse

1. She came from Greece, she had a thirst for know-ledge, she stud-ied sculp-ture at St.

(Verses 2–3(%) see block lyric)

Mar-tin's col-lege that's where I____ caught her eye.__

__ She told me that her

dad was load-ed. I said, in that case I'll have rum and Co-ca Co-la, she said, fine.__

__ And then in thir-ty sec-onds time__

she said, "I want to live like com - mon peo - ple,

I want to do what - ev - er com - mon peo - ple do. Want to sleep with

com - mon peo - ple, I want to sleep with com - mon peo - ple like you."

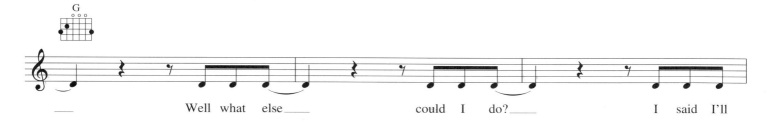

Well what else___ could I do?___ I said I'll

1.

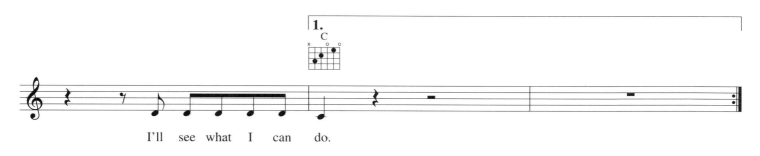

I'll see what I can do.

2,3.

(hand.) Rent a flat___ a - bove___ a shop,___

cut your hair___ and get___ a job,___ smoke some fags___

G

___ and play___ some pool,___ pre - tend you nev - er went___ to school,___

C

___ but still you'll nev - er get___ it right___ 'Cause when you're laid___

G

___ in bed___ at night___ watch - ing roach - es climb___ the wall,___

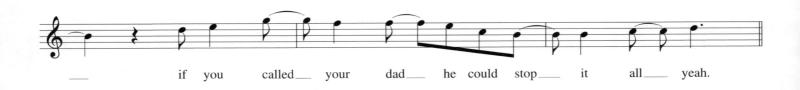

___ if you called___ your dad___ he could stop___ it all___ yeah.

Chorus

F

1.3. You'll nev - er live like com - mon peo - ple, you'll nev - er do what -

ev - er com - mon peo - ple do. You'll nev - er fail like com - mon peo - ple,

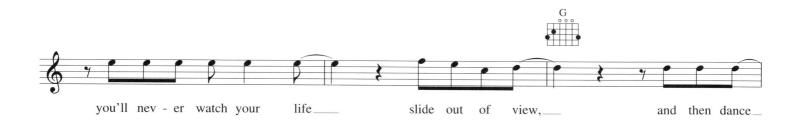

you'll nev - er watch your life___ slide out of view,___ and then dance___

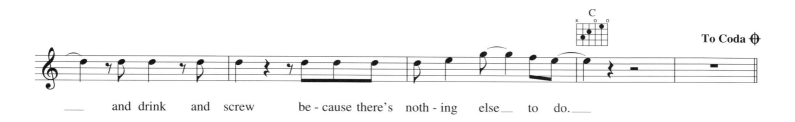

To Coda ⊕

___ and drink and screw be - cause there's noth - ing else___ to do.___

Instrumental

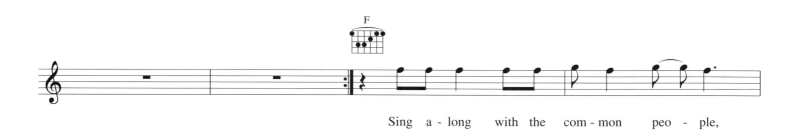

Sing a - long with the com - mon peo - ple,

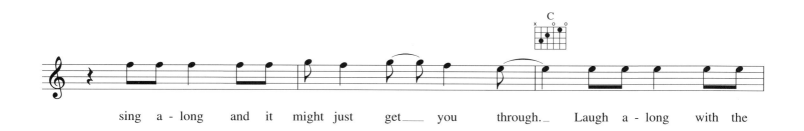

sing a - long and it might just get___ you through.___ Laugh a - long with the

com - mon peo - ple laugh a - long ev - en though they're laugh - in' at you___

and the stu - pid things___ that you do___ be - cause you think___

D. %. al Coda ⊕

___ that poor___ is cool.___

Coda ⊕

Want to live like com - mon peo - ple like you. Want to live like

1–4
com - mon peo - ple like you.

5.
Oh,_____ la,___ la, la,___ la.

Oh,_____ la,___ la, la,___ la.

Verse 2:
I took her to a supermarket
I don't know why
But I had to start it somewhere
So it started there
I said pretend you've got no money
She just laughed and said oh you're so funny
I said yeah?
Well I can't see anyone else smiling in here
And you sure you want to live like common people
You want to see whatever common people see
You want to sleep with common people
You want to sleep with common people like me
But she didn't understand
She just smiled and held my hand.

Verse 3:
Like a dog lying in the corner
They will bite you and never warn you
Look out,
They'll tear your insides out
'Cause everybody hates a tourist
Especially one who thinks it's all such a laugh
And the chip stains and grease
Will come out in the bath
You will never understand
How it feels to live your life
With no meaning or control
And with nowhere left to go
You're amazed that they exist
And they burn so bright that you can only wonder why.

D'You Know What I Mean?

Words & Music by Noel Gallagher

34

Verse 3:   I don't really care for what you believe
So open up your fist or you won't receive
The thoughts and the words of everyman you'll need.
So get up off the floor and believe in life
No-one's ever gonna ever ask you twice
Get on the bus and bring it on home to me.

Dancing Queen

Words & Music by Benny Andersson, Stig Anderson & Bjorn Ulvaeus

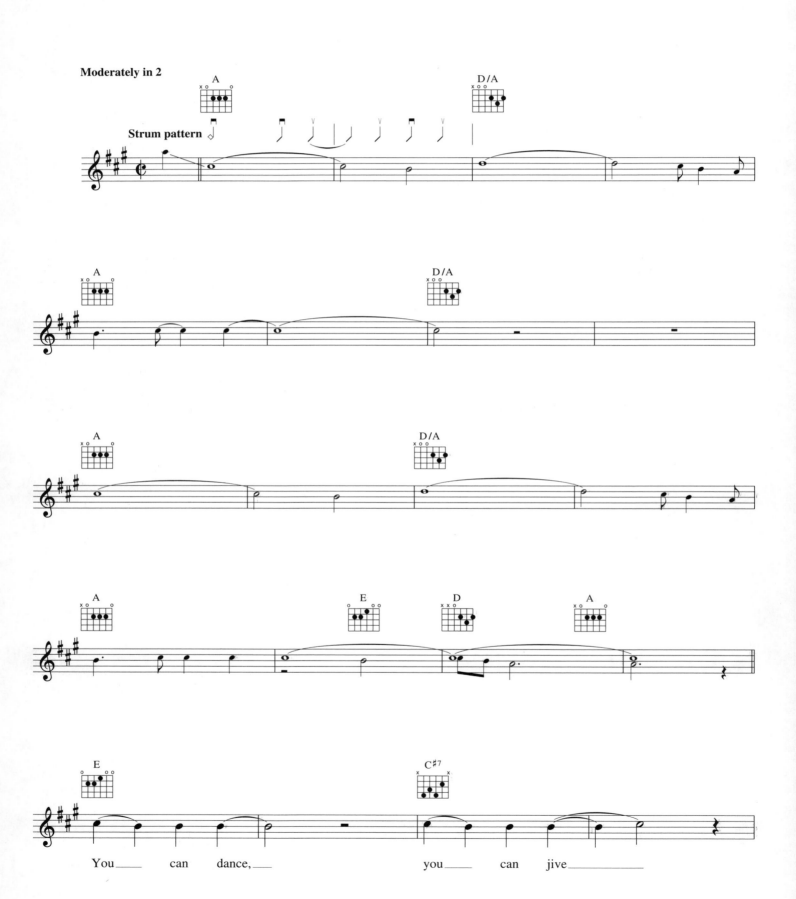

You___ can dance,___ you___ can jive_____

you come to look for a king. ____

Verse

An - y - bo - dy could see that guy ____
You're a tea - ser you turn them on ____

____ night is young ____ and the
____ leave 'em burn - ing and

mu - sic's high ____ With a bit ____ of rock
then you're gone ____ look - ing out ____ for an -

mu - sic ev - 'ry - thing ____ is fine
- oth - er an - y - one ____ will do
You're in the

mood for a dance ____ and when ____ you

get the ____ chance ____ You are ____ the

38

dancing queen young and sweet,

on - ly se - ven - teen

dancing queen,

feel the beat from the tam - bou - rine

Oh yeah, You can dance,

you can jive,

hav - ing the time of your life

Daniel

Words & Music by Elton John & Bernie Taupin

1.4. Dan - iel is trav - 'ling to - night___ on a plane___
2. They say Spain is pret - ty 'though I've___ nev - er been___
3. *Instrumental*

I can see the red___ tail lights___
Well Dan - iel says___ it's the best___ place he's

head - ing for Spa - in.___ Oh___ and   I can see Dan -
ev - er seen.___ Oh___ and   he should know___

- iel___ wav - ing good bye.___ God it looks___
he's___ been there e - nough.___ Lord___ I___

___ like Dan - iel, Must___ be the clouds.___
___ miss Dan - iel, Oh_____ I miss___

___ in___ my eyes.___
___ him___ so much.___

Oh_____ Dan - iel___ my broth - er___ you are

old - er___ than me,___ do you___ still feel the pain___

of the scars___ that___ won't heal,___ Your eyes___ have___ died___

42

Don't You (Forget About Me)

Words & Music by Keith Forsey & Steve Schiff

Every Breath You Take

Words & Music by Sting

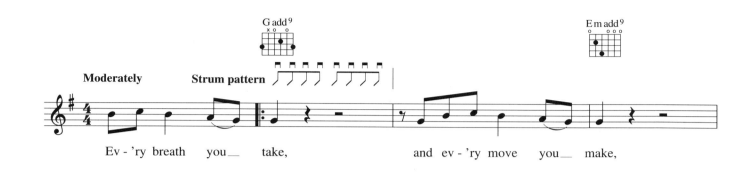

Ev - 'ry breath you___ take, and ev - 'ry move you___ make,

ev - 'ry bond___ you break,___ ev - 'ry step___ you take,___ I'll be watch - ing you.

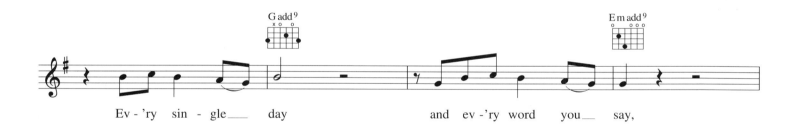

Ev - 'ry sin - gle___ day and ev - 'ry word you___ say,

ev - 'ry game___ you play,___ ev - 'ry night___ you stay___ I'll be watch - ing you.

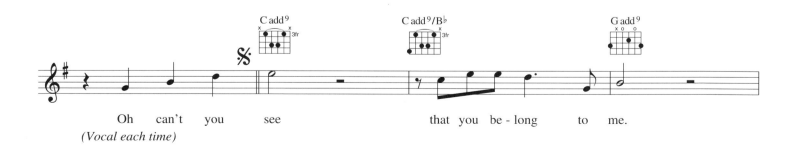

Oh can't you see that you be - long to me.

(Vocal each time)

How my poor heart___ aches_____ with ev-'ry step___ you

take. Ev-'ry move you___ make,

and ev-'ry vow you___ break, ev-'ry smile___ you fake,___

___ ev-'ry claim___ you stake,___ I'll be watch-ing you.

Since you've gone___ I've been lost___ with-out___ a trace,___

___ I dream at night, I can on-ly see___ your face.___

___ I look a-round but it's you I can't___ re-place,___ I feel so cold and I

long for your__ em-brace.__ I keep cry-ing ba-by, ba-by please__

Oh can't you

I'll be watch-ing__

you. Ev-'ry breath__ you take.__ ev-'ry move__ you make,__
2. Ev-'ry sin-gle day,__ ev-'ry word__ you say,__
3. Ev-'ry move you make,__ ev-'ry vow__ you break,__

Repeat to fade

__ ev-'ry bond__ you break,__ ev-'ry step you take.
ev-'ry game__ you play,__ ev-'ry night__ you stay.
ev-'ry smile you fake,__ ev-'ry claim you stake.

Ebony And Ivory

Words & Music by McCartney

i - vo - ry___ live to - ge - ther in per - fect har - mo - ny,___ side by

To Coda ⊕

side on my pia - no key - board, oh___ Lord, why___ don't we?___

Double Tempo

E - bo - ny,___ i - vo - ry, liv - ing in per - fect har - mo - ny,___

D. ％ al Coda ⊕

E - bo - ny,___ i - vo - ry___ ooh._____

⊕ Coda

Side by side on my pia - no key - board, oh___ Lord, why___

___ don't we?___

Double Tempo

Repeat to fade

E - bo - ny,___ i - vo - ry,___ liv - ing in per - fect har - mo - ny.

Eight Days A Week

Words & Music by John Lennon & Paul McCartney

ain't got noth - in' but love, 1,3,4. babe,_____ eight days a week._____
2. girl,_____

Bridge

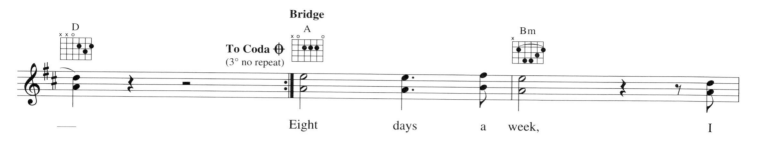

Eight days a week, I

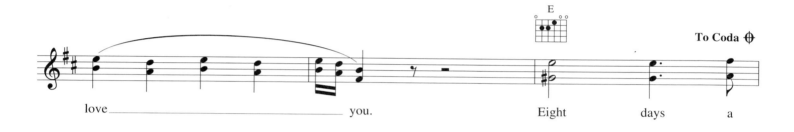

love_____ you. Eight days a

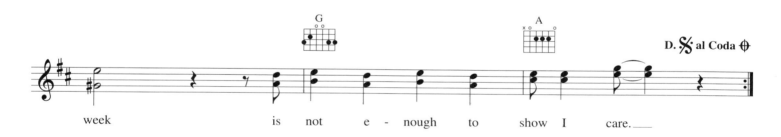

week is not e - nough to show I care._____

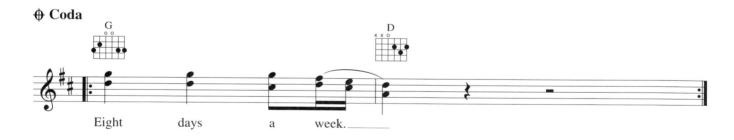

Eight days a week._____

Outro

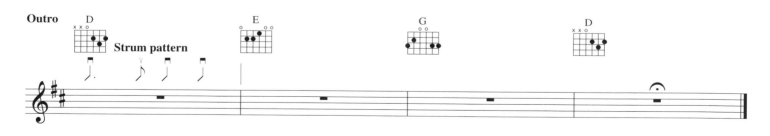

Everyday

Words & Music by Charles Hardin & Norman Petty

true love___ from___ me?___ 3. Ev - 'ry - day   it's___

___ a - get - tin' clos - er,   go - in' fast - er than___ a roll - er coast - er,

love   like___ yours will   sure - ly come___ my_____ way,   a - hey,___

a - hey, hey.

To Coda ⊕

Solo

D. 𝄋 al Coda ⊕

Coda ⊕

sure - ly come___ my_____ way,   a - hey,___   a - hey, hey,

poco rall.

love   like___ yours will_____ sure - ly come___ my_____ way.

Verse 2   Ev'ryday it's a-gettin' faster
               Everyone said go ahead and ask her
               Love like yours will surely come my way
               A-hey, a-hey, hey.

Everybody (Backstreet's Back)

Words & Music by Denniz Pop & Max Martin

♩ = 108

Intro

Strum pattern

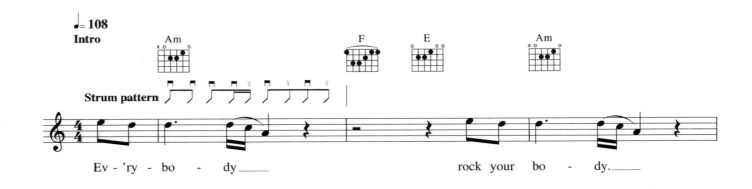

Ev - 'ry - bo - dy _____ rock your bo - dy. _____

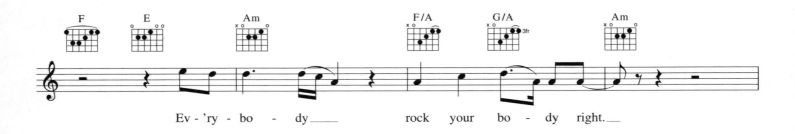

Ev - 'ry - bo - dy _____ rock your bo - dy right. _____

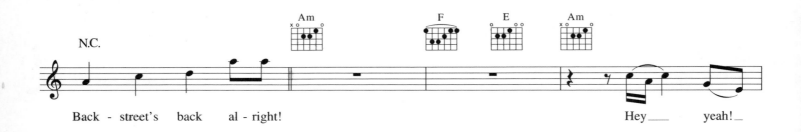

N.C.

Back - street's back al - right! Hey _____ yeah! _____

Now! _____ Oh my God _____ we're back a - gain, _____
(Verse 2 see block lyric)

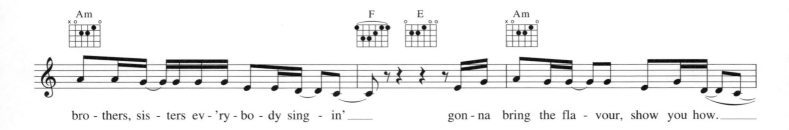

bro - thers, sis - ters ev - 'ry - bo - dy sing - in' _____ gon - na bring the fla - vour, show you how.

Verse 2:   Now throw your hands up in the air
And wave 'em around like you just don't care
If you wanna party let me hear you yell
'Cos we got it going on again.

Am I original *etc.*

(Everything I Do) I Do It For You

Words by Bryan Adams & Robert John 'Mutt' Lange. Music by Michael Kamen

you.

There's

Bridge

no love_____ like your love_____ and no__ oth – er could give

more____ love. There's no - where_____ un - less you're____ there all the

time,_____ all the way,___ yeah._____

1. **2.**

Oh, you can't tell me it's not worth try - in'

for, I can't help____ it, there's no - thing I want more. Yeah,__ I would

fight__ for you,__ I'd lie__ for you,__ walk the wire__ for you,__ yeah,__ I'd

die for__ you._____ You know it's true, ev - 'ry - thing I__

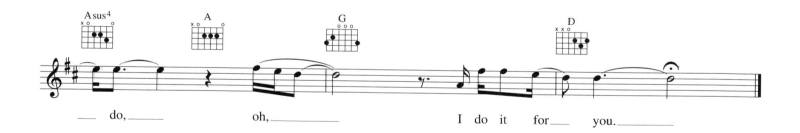

__ do,____ oh,_____ I do it for__ you._____

Verse 2: Look into your heart
You will find there's nothing there to hide
Take me as I am
Take my life
I would give it all
I would sacrifice
Don't tell me
It's not worth fighting for
I can't help it
There's nothing I want more
You know it's true
Everything I do
I do it for you.

Good Vibrations

Words & Music by Brian Wilson & Mike Love

Girls And Boys

Words & Music by Damon Albarn, Graham Coxon, Alex James & David Rowntree

Verse 2:
Avoiding all work
Because there's none available
Like battery thinkers
Count their thoughts on 1 2 3 4 5 fingers
Nothing is wasted
Only reproduced
You get nasty blisters
Du bist sehr schön
But we haven't been introduced.

Hanging On The Telephone

Words & Music by Jack Lee

Middle

Instr.

D. 𝄋 al Coda ⊕

(4.) I had to in - ter - rupt and

⊕ **Coda**

hang   up there un - re - lieved,   oh   hang

up there un - re - lieved,   oh   hang   up there un - re - lieved,

oh   hang   up there un - re - lieved,   oh_____

oh   un - re - lieved.

Heartbeat

Words & Music by Bob Montgomery & Norman Petty

I   know   that   true   love   will   be.
And   bring   to   me   love's   glo - ry.

Heart - beat,   why   do   you
Heart - beat,   why   do   you

miss   when   my   ba - by   kiss - es   me?
miss   when   my   ba - by   kiss - es   me?

1.

1. cont.

1. cont.   **2.**

Hotel California

Words & Music by Don Felder, Glenn Frey & Don Henley

Moderate rock beat

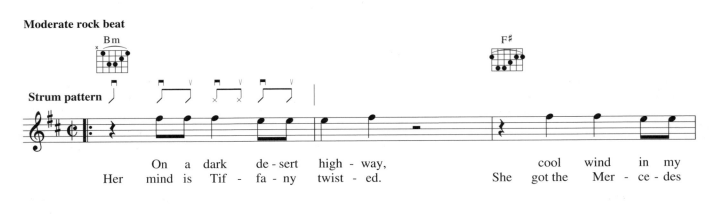

On a dark de - sert high - way,   cool wind in my
Her mind is Tif - fa - ny twist - ed.   She got the Mer - ce - des

hair,   warm smell of co - li - tas
bends.   She got a lot of pret - ty, pretty boys

ris - ing up through the air.   Up a - head in the
that she calls friends.   How they dance in the

dis - tance   I saw a shim - mer - ing light.
court - yard;   sweet sum - mer sweat.

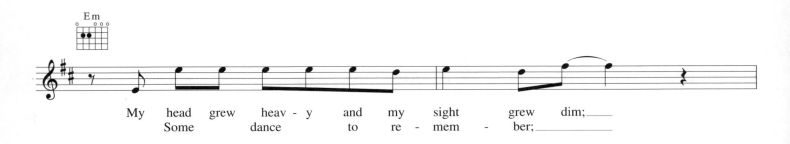

My head grew heav - y and my sight grew dim;
Some dance to re - mem - ber;

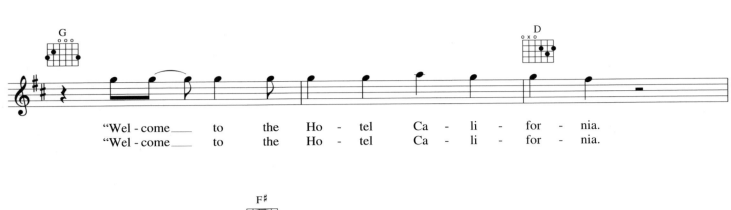

"Wel - come___ to the Ho - tel Ca - li - for - nia.
"Wel - come___ to the Ho - tel Ca - li - for - nia.

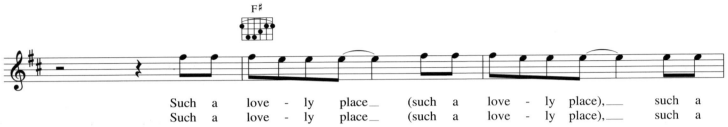

Such a love - ly place___ (such a love - ly place),___ such a
Such a love - ly place___ (such a love - ly place),___ such a

love - ly face.___ Plen - ty of room___ at the
love - ly face.___ liv - in' it up___ at the

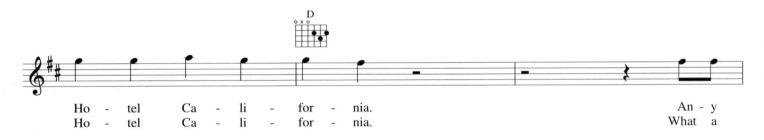

Ho - tel Ca - li - for - nia. An - y
Ho - tel Ca - li - for - nia. What a

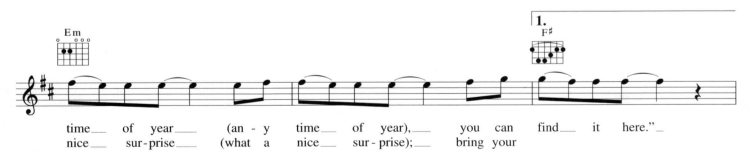

time___ of year___ (an - y time___ of year),___ you can find___ it here."___
nice___ sur - prise___ (what a nice___ sur - prise); bring your

a - li - bis."___

74

Mir - rors ___ on the ceil - ing, ___ the pink cham - pagne on
Last thing ___ I re - mem - ber, ___ I was run - ning for the

ice, ___ *and she said,* "We are all just
door. ___ I had to find the

pri - so - ners here ___ of our own ___ de - vice."
pas - sage back to the place I was ___ be - fore.

And in the mas - ter's ___ cham - bers, they gath - ered for the
"Re - lax," said the night man. "We are pro - grammed to re -

feast. They stab it ___ with their steel - y knives, ___ but they
- ceive. You can check out an - y time you like, ___ but

1. just can't ___ kill the beast.
2. you can nev - er leave."

D. 𝄋 *(instrumental) and fade*

75

I Shall Be Released

Words & Music by Bob Dylan & Richard Manuel

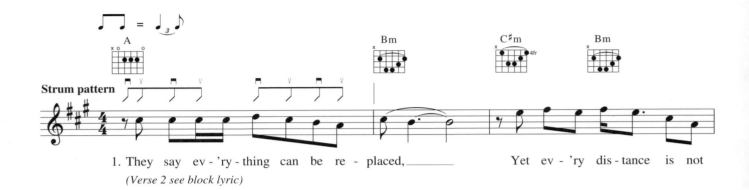

1. They say ev - 'ry - thing can be re - placed,

Yet ev - 'ry dis - tance is not

(Verse 2 see block lyric)

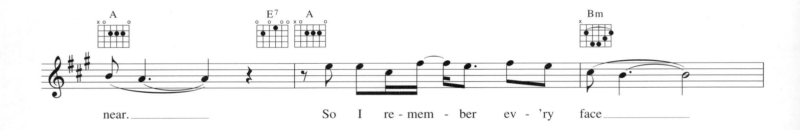

near.

So I re - mem - ber ev - 'ry face

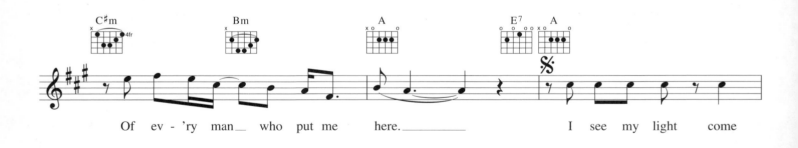

Of ev - 'ry man who put me here.

I see my light come

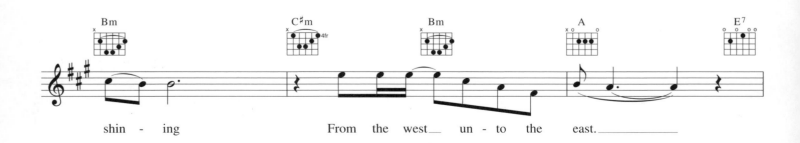

shin - ing

From the west un - to the east.

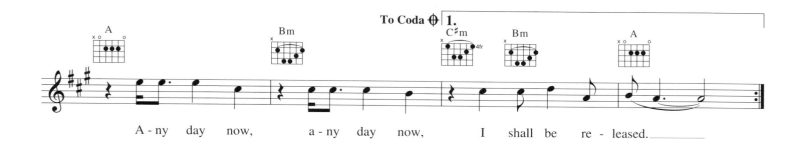

A - ny day now,   a - ny day now,   I   shall   be   re - leased._____

I   shall   be   re - leased._____   Stand - ing   next   to   me   in   this   lone - ly

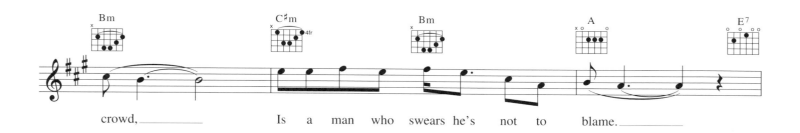

crowd,_____   Is   a   man   who   swears   he's   not   to   blame._____

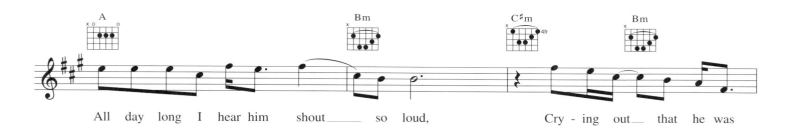

All   day   long   I   hear   him   shout_____   so   loud,   Cry - ing   out__   that   he   was

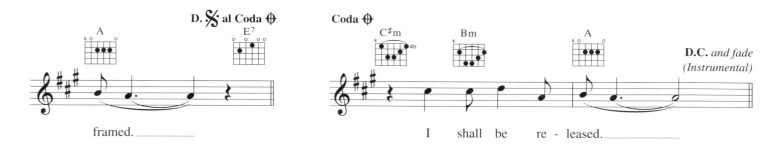

framed._____   I   shall   be   re - leased._____

Verse 2:   They say ev'ry man needs protection
They say ev'ry man must fall
Yet I swear I see my reflection
Some place so high above this wall.
I see my light *etc*.

I Shot The Sheriff

Words & Music by Bob Marley

Bright 4

1.4. I shot the she - riff, but I
2.3. I shot the she - riff, but I

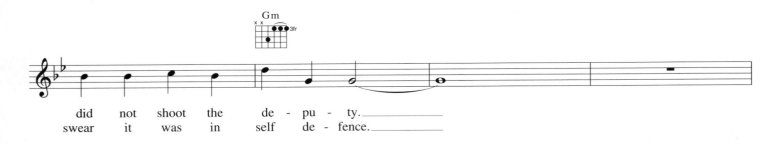

did not shoot the de - pu - ty.
swear it was in self de - fence.

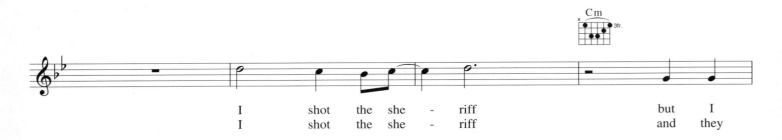

I shot the she - riff but I
I shot the she - riff and they

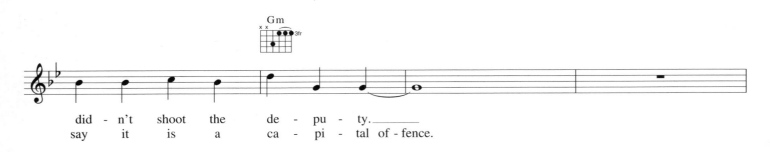

did - n't shoot the de - pu - ty.
say it is a ca - pi - tal of - fence.

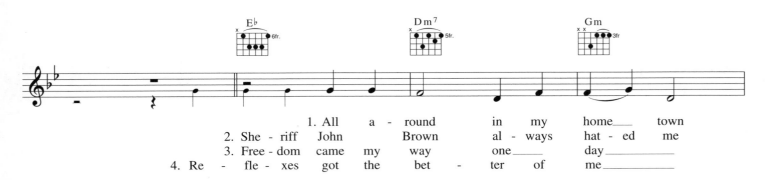

1. All a - round in my home town
2. She - riff John Brown al - ways hat - ed me
3. Free - dom came my way one day
4. Re - fle - xes got the bet - ter of me

Ironic

Music by Alanis Morissette & Glenn Ballard. Words by Alanis Morissette

* Symbols in parentheses represent chord names with respect to capoed guitar.
Symbols above reflect actual sounding chords.

Verse 2   Mister Play It Safe was afraid to fly
           He packed his suitcase and kissed his kids goodbye
           He waited his whole damn life to take that flight
           And as the plane crashed down he thought, "Well isn't this nice?"

           It's like the rain . . . *etc.*

Jamming

Words & Music by Bob Marley

Jealous Guy

Words & Music by John Lennon

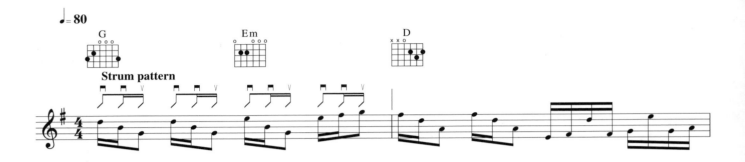

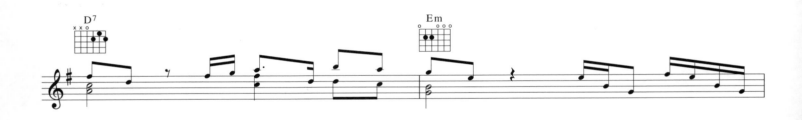

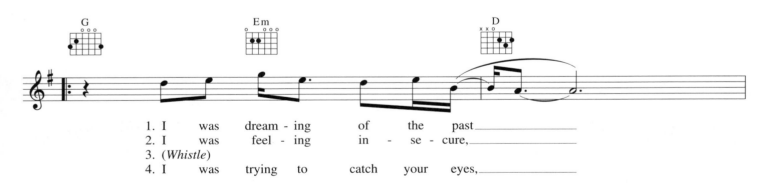

1. I was dream - ing of the past____
2. I was feel - ing in - se - cure,____
3. (Whistle)
4. I was trying to catch your eyes,____

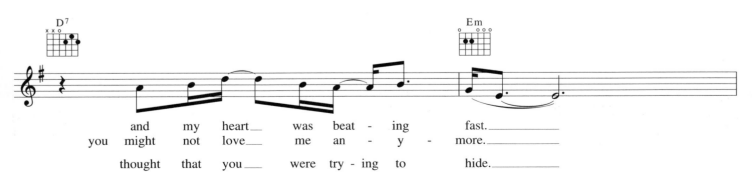

and my heart___ was beat - ing fast.____
you might not love___ me an - y - more.____

thought that you___ were try - ing to hide.____

Play 4 times

I be - gan to lose con - trol,
I was shiv - er - ing in - side,
I was swal - low - ing my pain,

I be - gan to lose con -
I was shiv - er - ing in -
I was swal - low - ing my

- trol
- side
pain

I did - n't mean to hurt you,

I'm sor - ry that I made you cry. Oh no, I did - n't want to hurt

you, I'm just a jea - lous guy.

I'm just a jea - lous guy, watch out, I'm just a jeal - ous guy, look out babe,

I'm just a jea - lous guy.

Just Like A Woman

Words & Music by Bob Dylan

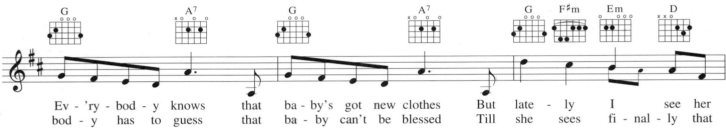

1. No - bod - y feels an - y pain, To - night as I stand in - side the rain,
Mar - y, she's my friend. Yes I be - lieve I'll go see her a - gain. No-

Ev - 'ry - bod - y knows that ba - by's got new clothes But late - ly I see her
bod - y has to guess that ba - by can't be blessed Till she sees fi - nal - ly that

rib - bons and her bows___ have fall - en from her curls. She
she's like all the rest___ with her fog, her am-phet-a -mine, ___ and her pearls.

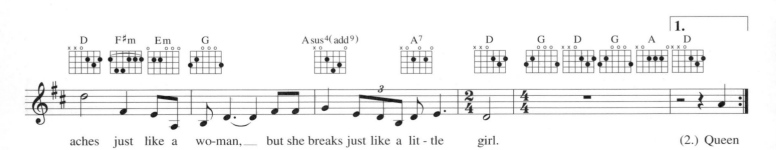

takes just like a wo - man yes, she does.___ She makes love just like a wo - man, yes, she does.___ And she

1.

aches just like a wo - man,___ but she breaks just like a lit - tle girl.   (2.) Queen

Lyin' Eyes

Words & Music by Don Henley & Glenn Frey

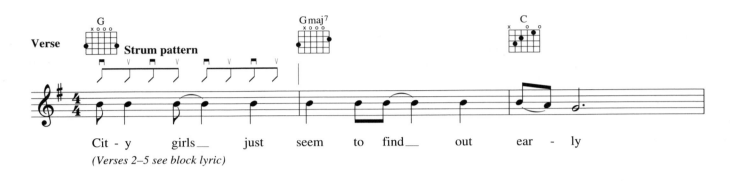

Cit - y girls___ just seem to find___ out ear - ly

(Verses 2–5 see block lyric)

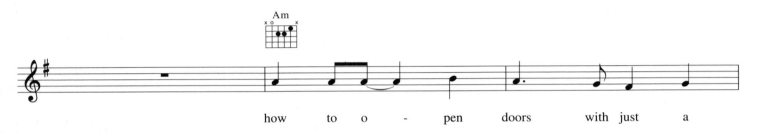

how to o - pen doors with just a

smile. A rich old man,___ and

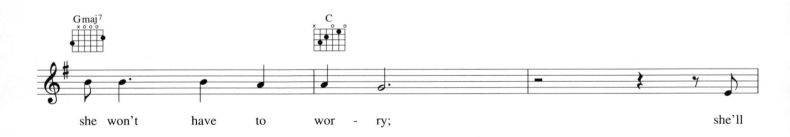

she won't have to wor - ry; she'll

dress up all in lace and go in style.

Verse 2: Late at night a big old house gets lonely
I guess every form of refuge has its price
And it breaks her heart to think her love is only
Given to a man with hands as cold as ice.

Verse 3: So she tells him she must go out for the evening
To comfort an old friend who's feelin' down
But he knows where she's goin' as she's leavin'
She is headed for the cheatin' side of town.

Verse 4: She gets up and pours herself a strong one
And stares out at the stars up in the sky
Another night, it's gonna be a long one
She draws the shade and hangs her head to cry.

Verse 5: My, oh my, you sure know how to arrange things
You set it up so well, so carefully
Ain't it funny how your new life didn't change things
You're still the same old girl you used to be.

In The Air Tonight

Words & Music by Phil Collins

1.

2.

all been a pack of lies.
stran - ger to you_____ or me.

⊕ **Coda**

I can feel it_____ in the air_____ to - night, oh Lord,_____

_____ oh Lord._____ Well, I've been wait - ing for this

mo - ment for all my life,_____ oh Lord._____

And I can feel it com - ing in the air to - night,_____ oh Lord._

Fade on repeat

Well I've been wait - ing for this

mo - ment for all my life,_____ oh Lord._____

Money For Nothing

Words & Music by Mark Knopfler & Sting

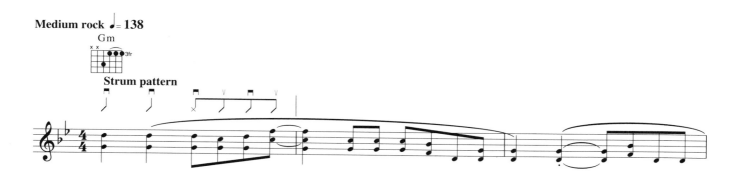

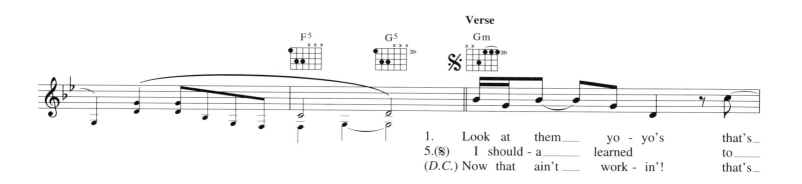

1. Look at them___ yo - yo's that's___
5.(%) I should - a___ learned to___
(D.C.) Now that ain't ___ work - in'! that's___

___ the way to do it,___ you play the gui - tar on the M. T. V.
___ play the gui - tar,___ I should - a learned to play them drums.
___ the way to do it,___ you play the gui - tar on the M. T. V.

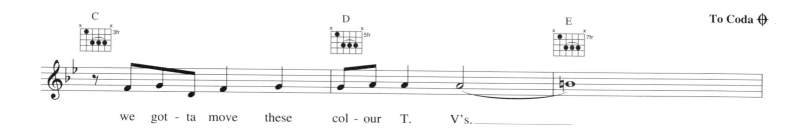

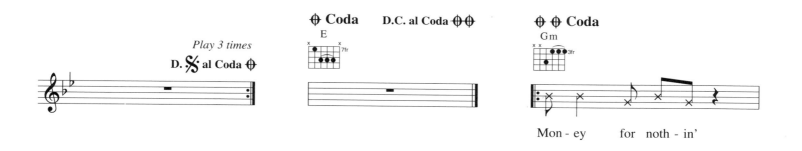

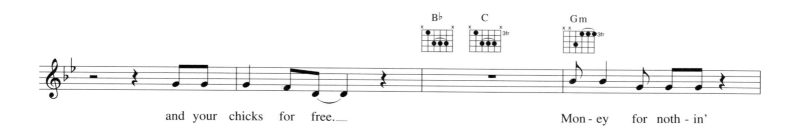

No More Heroes

Words & Music by Hugh Cornwell, Jean-Jacques Burnel, Jet Black & Dave Greenfield

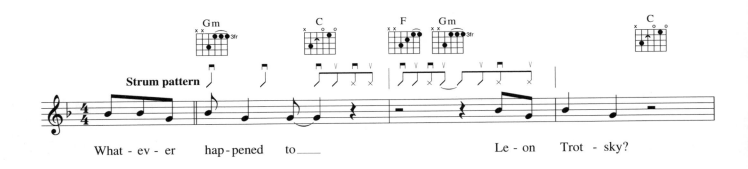

What - ev - er hap - pened to___ Le - on Trot - sky?

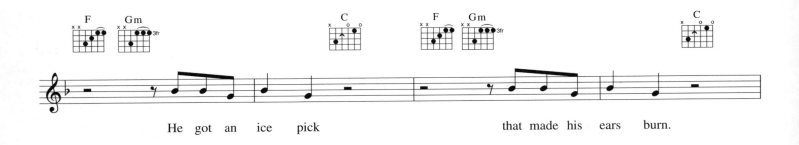

He got an ice pick that made his ears burn.

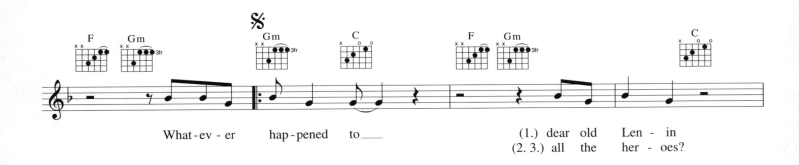

What - ev - er hap - pened to___ (1.) dear old Len - in
(2. 3.) all the her - oes?

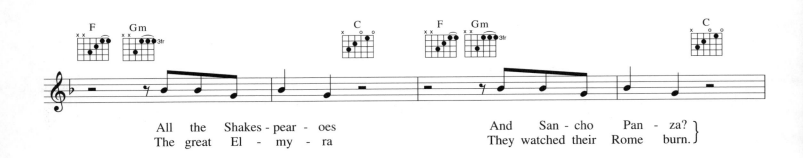

All the Shakes - pear - oes And San - cho Pan - za?
The great El - my - ra They watched their Rome burn.

What - ev - er hap - pened to_____ the

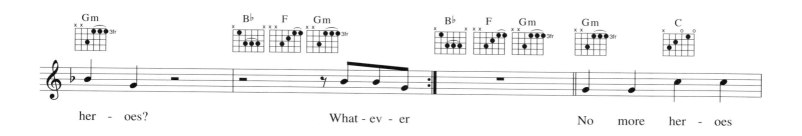

her - oes? What - ev - er No more her - oes

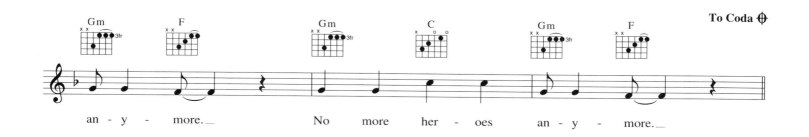

To Coda ⊕

an - y - more.__ No more her - oes an - y - more.__

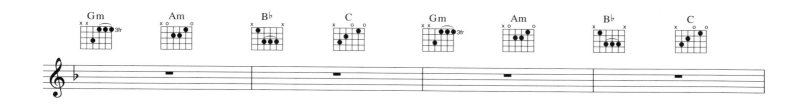

D. %. al Coda ⊕

⊕ **Coda**

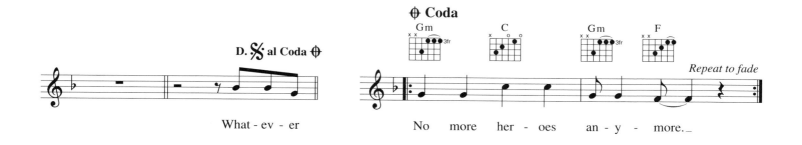

What - ev - er

Repeat to fade

No more her - oes an - y - more.__

One More Night

Words & Music by Phil Collins

help   me_____   back_____   so   I   can   make   you
then   I_____   thought__   may - be   you're   make   not   a -
know   that   I'll   be   here,   and   may-be   we   both   can

To Coda ⊕

see._____ ⎫
- lone._____ ⎬
learn._____ ⎭   Please__   give   me   one   more   night.__

Give   me   one   more   night,___

one   more   night,___   'cause   I   can't__   wait   for - ev - er.

Give   me   just   one   more   night,___   just

one   more   night, __   oh,__   one   more   night,___   'cause   I   can't__

wait for - ev - er.

1.

2. Give me

one_____ more night._____ Give me just one more night,_____

_____ one more night_____ 'cause I_____

_____ can't wait_____ for - ev - er._____ Like a riv -

- er to_____ the sea,_____ I will al - ways be_____ with

you. And if_____ you sail a - way,_____ I will fol - low you._____

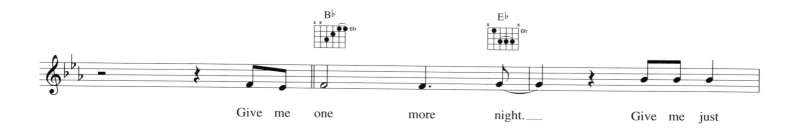

Give me one more night.___ Give me just

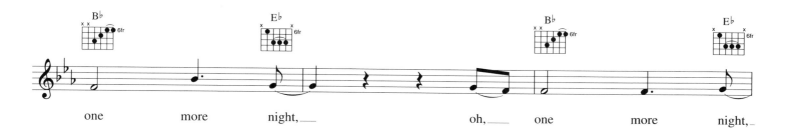

one more night,___ oh,___ one more night,_

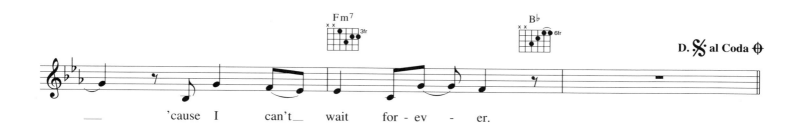

_ 'cause I can't_ wait for - ev - er.

⊕ Coda

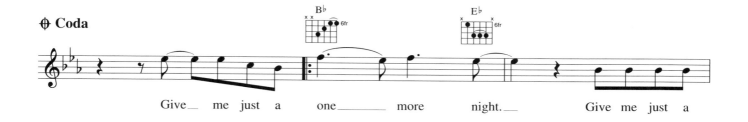

Give_ me just a one____ more night.___ Give me just a

one more night,___ one more night,_

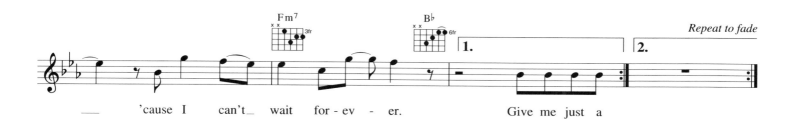

_ 'cause I can't_ wait for - ev - er. Give me just a

103

Norwegian Wood

Words & Music by John Lennon & Paul McCartney

Verse 2:   She told me she worked in the morning and started to laugh
I told her I didn't and crawled off to sleep in the bath
And when I awoke I was alone this bird had flown
So I lit a fire, isn't it good, Norwegian wood?

Paperback Writer

Words & Music by John Lennon & Paul McCartney

Pa - per - back wri - ter,_____ wri - ter,_____

Strum pattern   let ring _ _ _ _ _ _ _ _ _   sim.

1. Dear__ Sir or Ma - dam will you
(Verses 2-4 see block lyric)

read my book, it took me years to write_ will you take a look? It's

based on a no - vel by a man named Lear and I need a job__ so I

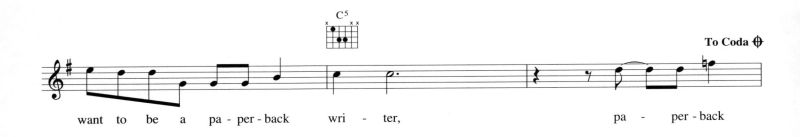

To Coda

want to be a pa - per - back wri - ter, pa - per - back

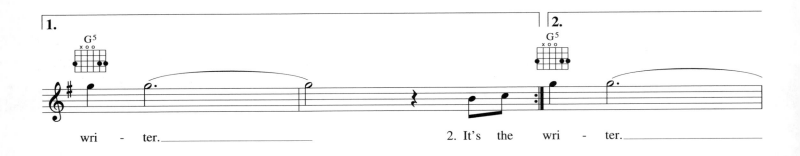

1.

wri - ter._____

2.

2. It's the wri - ter._____

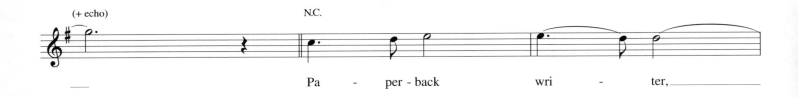

(+ echo)   N.C.

_____   Pa - per - back wri - ter,_____

D. %; al Coda
with repeats

3. It's a

106

⊕ Coda

wri - ter.   pa - per-back wri - ter,

Pa - per-back

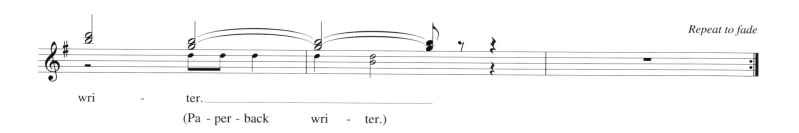

Repeat to fade

wri - ter.

(Pa - per - back   wri - ter.)

Verse 2:

It's the dirty story of a dirty man
And his clinging wife doesn't understand
His son is working for the Daily Mail
It's a steady job, but he wants to be a paperback writer
Paperback writer.

Verse 3:(%)

It's a thousand pages, give or take a few
I'll be writing more in a week or two
I can make it longer if you like the style
I can change it round, and I want to be a paperback writer
Paperback writer.

Verse 4:

If you really like it you can have the rights
It could make a million for you overnight
If you must return it you can send it here
But I need a break, and I want to be a paperback writer
Paperback writer.

Pinball Wizard

Words & Music by Peter Townshend

Brightly

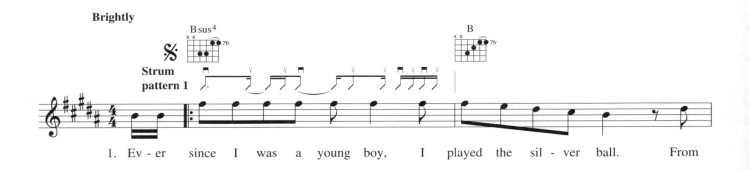

1. Ev - er since I was a young boy, I played the sil - ver ball. From

So - ho down to Brigh - ton, I must have played 'em all. But I ain't seen noth - ing like him in

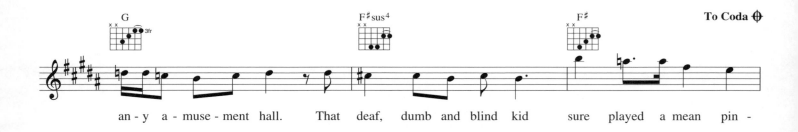

an - y a - muse - ment hall. That deaf, dumb and blind kid sure played a mean pin -

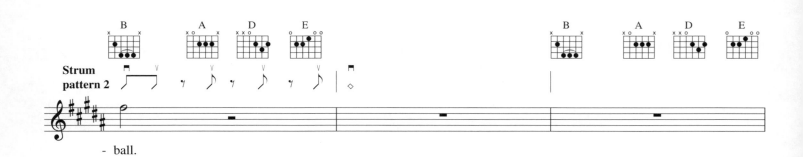

- ball.

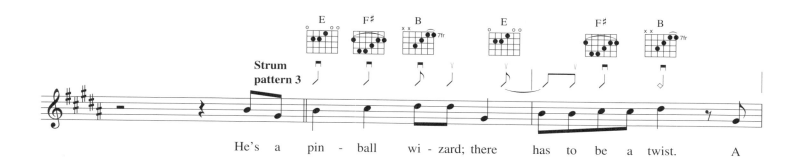

He's a pin - ball wi - zard; there has to be a twist. A

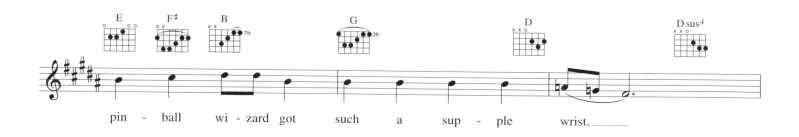

pin - ball wi - zard got such a sup - ple wrist._____

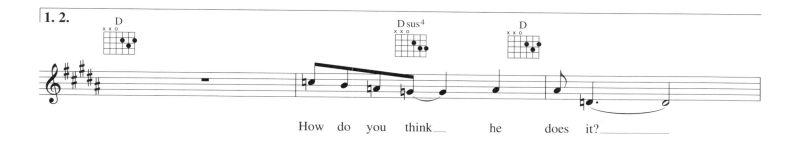

1. 2.

How do you think____ he does it?_____

D. 𝄋 al Coda ⊕ ⊕ **Coda**

3.

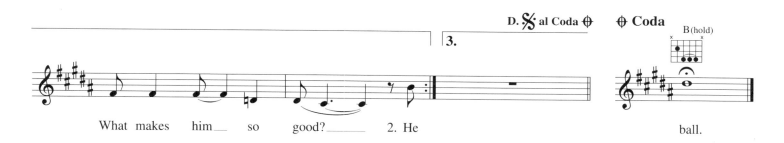

What makes him____ so good?____ 2. He

ball.

Verse 2:   He stands like a statue, becomes part of the machine
Feeling all the bumpers, always playing clean
Feels by intuition; the digit counters fall
That deaf, dumb and blind kid sure plays a mean pinball
He's a pinball wizard etc.

Verse 3:   Ain't got no distractions, can't hear no buzzers and bells
Don't see no lights a-flashin'; plays by sense of smell
Always gets a replay; never tilts at all
That deaf, dumb and blind kid sure plays a mean pinball
I thought I was the Bally table king,
But I just handed my pinball crown to him.

Verse 4:   Even on my favourite table, he can beat my best
His disciples lead him in, and he just does the rest
He's got crazy, flippin' fingers; never seen him fail
That deaf, dumb and blind kid sure plays a mean pinball.

Proud Mary

Words & Music by John C. Fogerty

1. Left a good job in the ci - ty, work - in' for the man ev - 'ry
2. Cleaned lot of plates in Mem - phis, pumped a lot of pain down in
3. *Guitar Solo*
(Verse 4 see block lyric)

night and day and I nev - er lost one min - ute of sleep - in',
New Or - leans, but I nev - er saw the good side of the ci - ty,

wor - ry - in' 'bout the way things might have been. Big wheel a - keep on turn -
'til I hitched a ride on a riv - er boat queen.

Verse 4:   If you come down to the river
         Bet you're gonna find some people who live
         You don't have to worry
         'Cause you have no money
         People on the river are happy to give
         Big wheel keep on turnin'
         Proud Mary keep on burnin'
         Rollin', rollin', rollin' on the river.

Private Investigations

Words & Music by Mark Knopfler

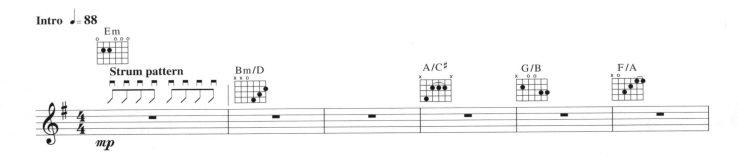

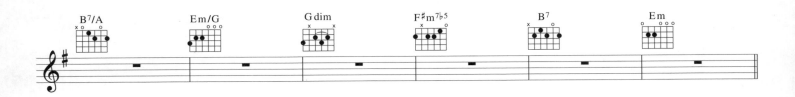

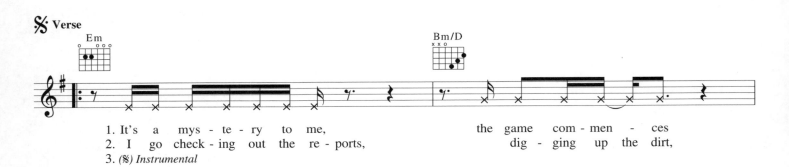

1. It's a mys-te-ry to me,   the game com-men-ces
2. I go check-ing out the re-ports,   dig-ging up the dirt,
3. (%) *Instrumental*

for the us-u-al fee,___   plus ex-pens-es
you get to meet all sorts   in this line of work,

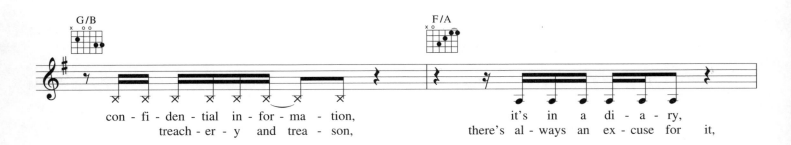

con-fi-den-tial in-for-ma-tion,   it's in a di-a-ry,
treach-er-y and trea-son,   there's al-ways an ex-cuse for it,

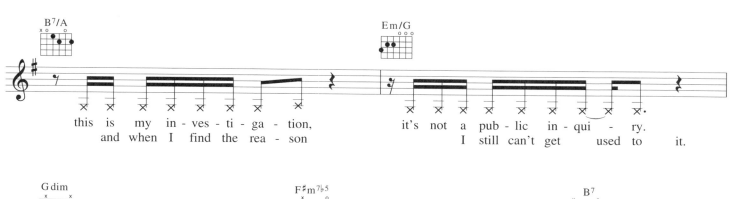

this is my in - ves - ti - ga - tion,   it's not a pub - lic in - qui - ry.
and when I find the rea - son   I still can't get   used to it.

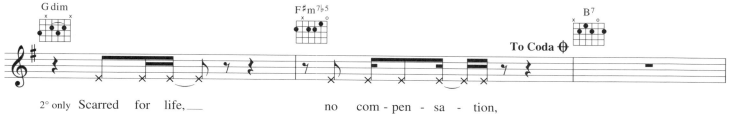

2° only Scarred for life,___   no com - pen - sa - tion,

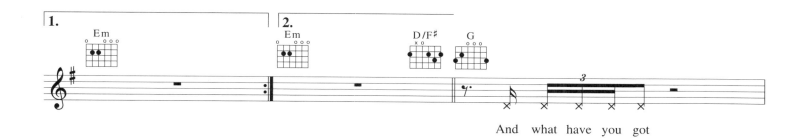

And what have you got

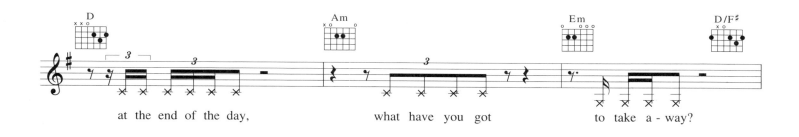

at the end of the day,   what have you got   to take a - way?

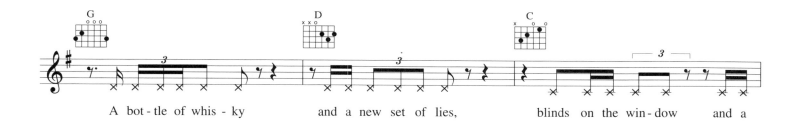

A bot - tle of whis - ky   and a new set of lies,   blinds on the win - dow   and a

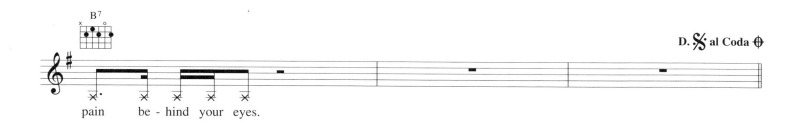

pain be - hind your eyes.

pri - vate   in - ves - ti - ga - tions.

Remember How We Started

Words & Music by Paul Weller

Outro

Sailing

Words & Music by Gavin Sutherland

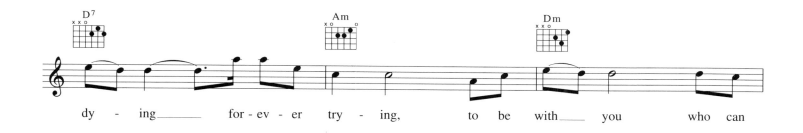

dy - ing____ for - ev - er try - ing, to be with____ you who can

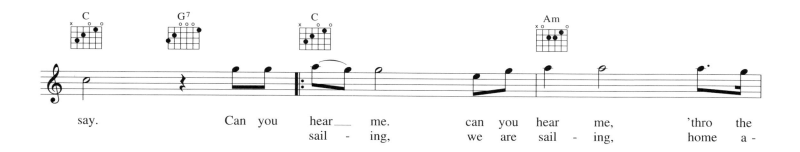

say. Can you hear____ me. can you hear me, 'thro the
sail - ing, we are sail - ing, home a-

dark____ night far a - way? I am dy - ing____ for - ev - er
- gain____ 'cross the sea. We are sail - ing,____ stor - my

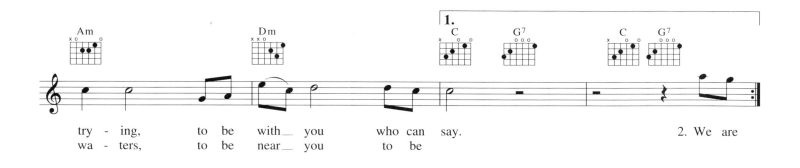

try - ing, to be with__ you who can say. 2. We are
wa - ters, to be near__ you to be

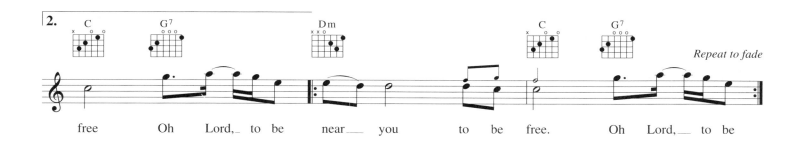

free Oh Lord,__ to be near____ you to be free. Oh Lord,__ to be

She Bangs The Drums

Words & Music by Ian Brown & John Squire

Intro

♩ = 138

Strum pattern

Drum intro

Fig 1 . . .

Verse

I can feel the earth___ be - gin___ to move,___ I hear my nee-

I don't feel too stea - dy on___ my feet,___ I feel hol -

- dle hit___ the groove,___ and spi - ral through___ an - oth - er day,

- low I___ feel weak___ pas - sion fruit___ and ho - ly bread

___ I hear my song___ be - gin___ to say___ "Kiss me where

___ fill my guts___ and ease___ my head   Through the ear -

___ the sun don't shine,___ the past was yours___ but the fu - ture's

- ly morn - ing sun,___ I can see___ her, here she

mine,_____ you're all____ out of time."_____
comes,_____ she____ bangs the

1. _____ **2.** drums._____

𝄋 **Chorus**

Have____ you seen____ her, have____ you heard?____ The way she plays,____

____ there are____ no words____ to des - cribe____ the way____ I

feel._____ How could it ev -

- er come____ to pass?____ She'll be the first,____ she'll be____ the last,____

To Coda 𝄌

____ to des - cribe____ the way____ I feel,_____

the way I feel

A   E

A   E

E

D. 𝄋 al Coda ⊕

1.   **2.** E

D

⊕ Coda

the way I feel.

A   D   A   D

Have____ you seen____ her, have____ you heard?____ The way she plays,____

there are no words to des - cribe the way I

feel. How could it ev -

- er come to pass? She'll be the first, she'll be the last

to des - cribe the way I feel,

the way I feel.

Repeat to fade

123

Saturday Night

Words & Music by Brett Anderson & Richard Oakes

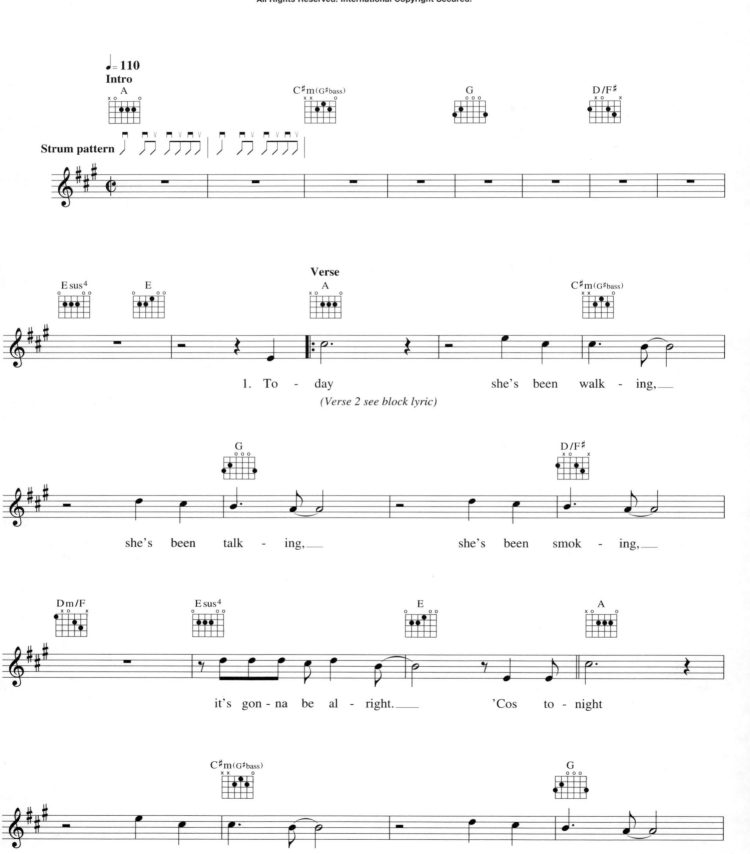

we'll get car sick, and it-'ll be o -

- kay like ev-'ry-one says, it-'ll be al - right, and ev - er so

nice. We're go - ing out to - night, out and a -

%: Chorus

- bout to - night. Oh, what - ev - er makes her hap - py

on a Sa - tur - day night. Oh, what - ev - er makes her hap - py,

To Coda ⊕

1. **2.**

what - ev - er makes it al - right. Ah. 2. To Ah.

We'll go to freak shows and peep shows. (Ah.)

125

Verse 2:   Today she's been sat there, sat there in a black chair, office furniture
But it'll be alright
'Cos tonight we'll go drinking, we'll do silly things, and never let the winter in
And it'll be okay like everyone says, it'll be alright and ever so nice
We're going out tonight, out and about tonight.

Stayin' Alive

Words & Music by Barry Gibb, Robin Gibb & Maurice Gibb

Medium Rock beat

Well, you can tell_

(1.3.) _ by the way I walk_ my walk, I'm a wom - an's man: no time to talk.
(2.) _ get_ low and I get high,_ and if I _ can't get ei - ther, I real - ly try._ Got the

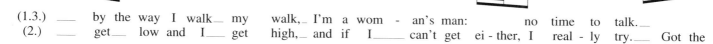

mu - sic loud_ and wom - en warm, I've been kicked a - round_ since I_ was born. And now it's
wings of heav - en on_ my shoes,_ I'm a danc - in' man_ and I just can't lose._ You know it's

all right._ It's O. K._ and you may look_ the oth - er way._
all right._ It's O. K._ I'll live to see_ an - oth - er day._

We can try_ to un - der - stand_ the New York Times' ef - fect_ on man.

Wheth - er you're a broth - er or wheth - er you're a moth - er, you're stay - in' a - live.___ stay - in' a - live.___

Feel the ci - ty break - in' and ev - 'ry - bo - dy shak - in', and we're stay - in' a - live,___ stay - in' a - live.___

Ah, ha, ha, ha, stay - in' a - live,___ stay - in' a - live.___ Ah, ha, ha, ha,

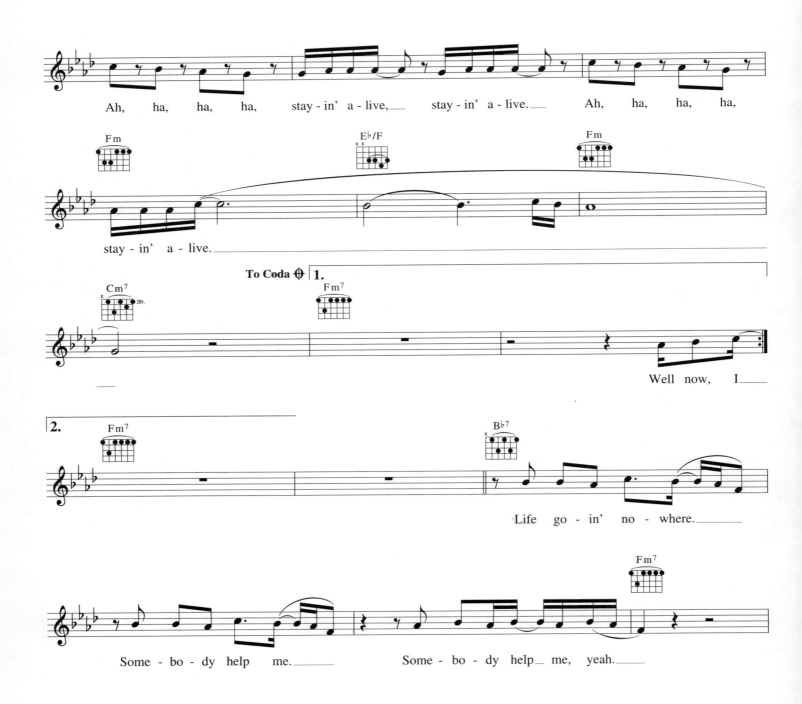

stay - in' a - live.___

To Coda ⊕ **1.**

Well now, I___

2.

Life go - in' no - where.___

Some - bo - dy help me.___ Some - bo - dy help me, yeah.___

Still Crazy After All These Years

Words & Music by Paul Simon

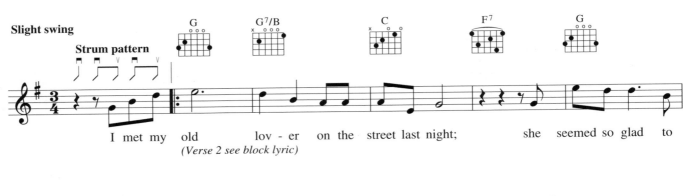

I met my old lov - er on the street last night; she seemed so glad to

(Verse 2 see block lyric)

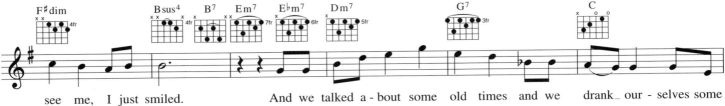

see me, I just smiled. And we talked a - bout some old times and we drank_ our - selves some

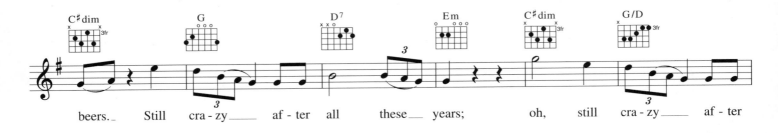

beers._ Still cra - zy____ af - ter all these____ years; oh, still cra - zy____ af - ter

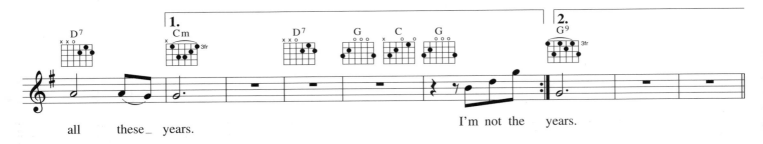

all these_ years. I'm not the years.

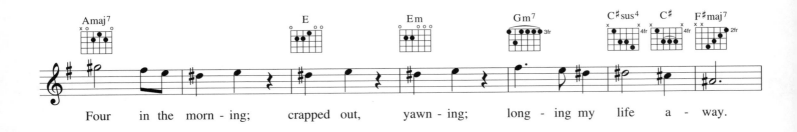

Four in the morn - ing; crapped out, yawn - ing; long - ing my life a - way.

Verse 2: I'm not the kind of man who tends to socialize
I seem to lean on old familiar ways
That whisper in my ears
Still crazy after all these years.

Tears In Heaven

Words & Music by Eric Clapton & Will Jennings

Gentle, moderate beat

Strum pattern

Verse

1. Would you know my name _____ if I saw you in hea-

(Verses 2–3 see block lyric)

-ven? Would you be the same _____

if I saw you in hea - ven? I must be strong ___

___ and car - ry on, ___ 'cause I

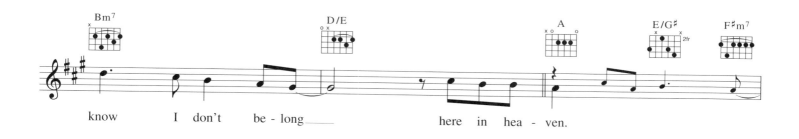

know   I don't be - long_____   here in hea - ven.

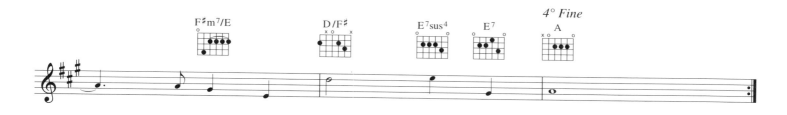

4° Fine

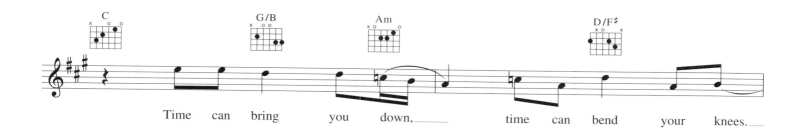

Time can bring you down,_____   time can bend your knees.___

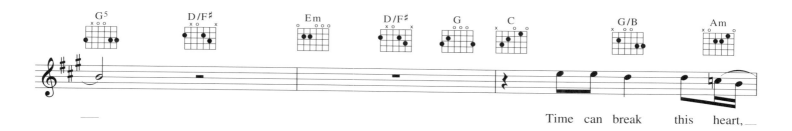

Time can break this heart,___

D. % *(Repeat)*

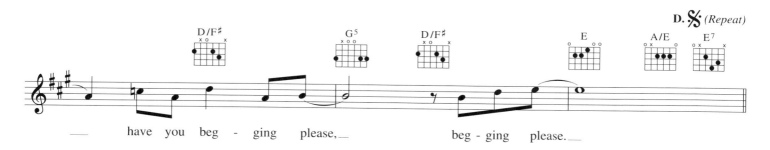

___ have you beg - ging please,   beg - ging please.___

Verse 2:

Would you hold my hand
If I saw you in heaven?
Would you help me stand
If I saw you in heaven?
I'll find my way
Through night and day
'Cause I know I just can't stay
Here in heaven.

Verse 3:

Instrumental solo – 8 bars

Beyond the door
There's peace, I'm sure
And I know there'll be no more
Tears in heaven.

Verse 4 (D.S.):

Would you know my name
If I saw you in heaven?
Would you be the same
If I saw you in heaven?
I must be strong
And carry on
'Cause I know I don't belong
Here in heaven.

The Day We Caught The Train

Words & Music by Steve Cradock, Damon Minchella, Oscar Harrison & Simon Fowler

Em   A

look - ing at the trees   on the road - side, feel - ing it's a ho - li - day.

D   A#dim   Bm

You and   I___   should ride___ the coast___ and wind___ up in our

A/C#   Em   G

fav - 'rite coats just   miles a - way.   Roll a num -

A

- ber,   write an - oth - er song like Jim - my heard___ the day___

A/C#   **Chorus** D   A

___ he caught___ the train.___   Oh___   la   la,___

G   Em   D   A

___ oh___   la   la.___   Oh___   la   la,___

G   Em   **1.**   **2.**

___ oh___   la.

You and I should ride the tracks and find our- selves just wad-

- ing through to- mor - row.

And you and I when we're com- ing down, we're on- ly get- ting back and you know

I feel no sor - row. Oh la la,

oh la la. Oh la la,

oh la When you find that things

are get- ting wild, but don't you want days like these.

Verse 2:

He sipped another rum and Coke and told a dirty joke
Walking like Groucho, sucking on a number 10
Rolling on the floor with the cigarette burns walked in
I'll miss the crush and I'm home again
Stepping through the door
With the night in store, whiling just an hour away
Step into the sky in the star bright feeling it's a brighter day.

The Riverboat Song

Words & Music by Simon Fowler, Steve Cradock, Oscar Harrison & Damon Minchella

1. I see dou - ble   up a -

(Verses 2 - 4 see block lyric)

head,   where the ri - ver-boat swayed be - neath the sun

    is where the ri - ver runs red.   Like a

king who stalks the wings and shoots a dove and kills an ea - gle in -

- stead,   It's more or less the same as the

1.

things that you said.

1. cont.

2. I see

2. 3. Chorus

♩ = 78

Strum pattern 2

And a - ny - way   for all the things you know,   tell me why does the ri - ver not

flow? And a - ny - way_____ for all the things you said, tell me why does the ri - ver run

red? And a - ny - way_____ for all the things you've seen, tell me when will the ri - ver run_____

green? And a - ny - way for all the things you know, tell me why does the ri - ver not flow?

D. 𝄋 al Coda ⨁

⨁ Coda

dou - ble, that's my trou - ble.

Repeat to fade

Verse 2: I see trouble up the road
 Like the things you found in love are by the way
 And like to cheat on your soul
 Like the best and worst of thoughts that lose control
 Before you lie on your bed
 It's more or less the same as the things that you said.

Verse 3: *Instrumental 4 bars*
 It's more or less the things you fail to say in your way
 That's your trouble
 Like a king that stalks the wings
 And shoots the moon and the stars and his double
 It's more or less the same as the things that you said.

Verse 4: (D.𝄋) I see double up ahead
 Where the riverboat swayed beneath the sun
 Is where the river runs red
 I see double, that's my trouble.

Tupelo Honey

Words & Music by Van Morrison

Verse

Capo 1st fret
Slowly

Strum pattern

1. You can take all the tea in Chi - na, put it in a big brown bag for me;

(Verses 2 & 3 see block lyric)

* Symbols in parentheses represent chord names with respect to capoed guitar
Symbols above represent actual sounding chords.

sail right round all the sev - en o - ceans, drop it straight in - to ___ the deep blue sea.

Chorus

She's as sweet as tu - pe - lo ho - ney, she's an - an - gel of the first de - gree.

1.,2.

3. D. and fade

She's as sweet as tu - pe - lo hon - ey, just like hon - ey. ba - by, from the bee. from the bee.

Verse 2: You can't stop us on the road to freedom
You can't keep us 'cause our eyes can see
Men with insight, men in granite
Knights in armour bent on chivalry.

Verse 3: I'll tell a tale of old Manhattan
Adirondack bus to go
Standing waiting on my number
And my number's gonna show.

Where The Streets Have No Name

Words & Music by U2

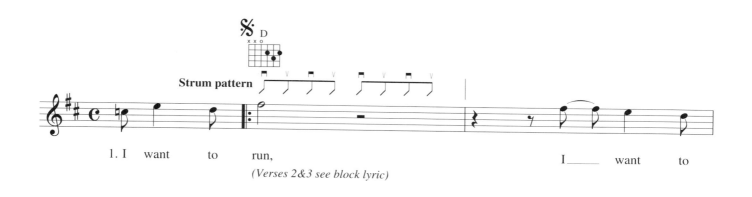

1. I want to run, I want to

(Verses 2&3 see block lyric)

hide, I want to tear down the walls

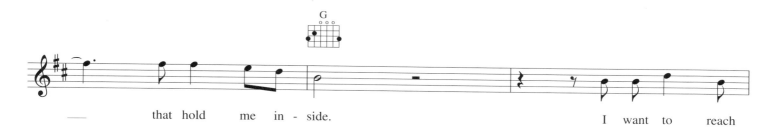

that hold me in - side. I want to reach

out and touch the flame

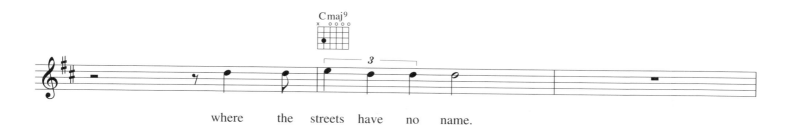

where the streets have no name.

2. I ____ want to where the streets have no

name, where the streets have no name.

We're still build - ing, then burn - ing ____ down love,

burn - ing ____ down love, and when I go there,

To Coda ⊕

I go there with you, it's all I can

D. %. al Coda ⊕

do. 3. The cit - y's a

Coda ⊕

It's all I can do.

Our love___ turns to rust we're beat-en and

blown by the wind,___ blown___ by the

1. wind **2.** wind, oh when I go there

I go there with you, it's all I can

do.

Repeat ad lib to fade

Verse 2: I want to feel sunlight on my face
See that dust cloud disappear without a trace
I want to take shelter from the poison rain
Where the streets have no name.

Verse 3: The city's a flood
And our love turns to rust
We're beaten and blown by the wind
Trampled in dust
I'll show you a place
High on a desert plain
Where the streets have no name.

Walking On The Moon

Words & Music by Sting

Chorus

Some may say I'm wish - ing my days a - way

no way and if it's the price I pay

some say to - mor - row's an - oth - er day

you'll stay I may as well play

Coda

Keep it up Keep it up.

Waterloo Sunset

Words & Music by Raymond Douglas Davies

Words

Words & Music by Barry Gibb, Robin Gibb & Maurice Gibb

all   to   me.   And   I   will   give you all   my

life.   I'm here if you should call   to   me.   You

think   that I don't ev - en mean   a sin - gle word I say.

It's   on - ly   words,   and words are all I have   to take your heart a -

- way.   It's   on - ly   words,   and words are all I

have   to take your heart a - way.   It's on - ly

words,   and words are all I have   to take your heart a - way.

Wonderwall

Words & Music by Noel Gallagher

never really had a doubt.____ I don't believe____ that an - y - bo - dy

feels the way I do____ a - bout you now.____ And all____

____ the roads____ we have____ to walk____ are wind - ing and all____

____ the lights____ that lead____ us there____ are blind - ing.

There are ma - ny things____ that I____ would like to say to you____ but I don't know how.

Chorus

{ Be - cause }
{ I said } may - be____

you're gon - na be the one that saves me,____ and af - ter all____

151

youʼre my won-der-wall. _____

1.

2.

I said may-be _____

youʼre gon-na be the one that saves me, _____ and af-ter all _____

youʼre my won-der-wall. _____

I said may-be _____ youʼre gon-na be the one that

Play 7 times

saves me, _____ youʼre gon-na be the one that

Vocal 1° & 2° only

Verse 3:

Today was gonna be the day
But theyʼll never throw it back to you
By now you shouldʼve somehow
Realised what youʼre not to do
I donʼt believe that anybody
Feels the way I do
About you now.

And all the roads that lead you there were winding
And all the lights that light the way are blinding
There are many things that I would like to say to you
But I donʼt know how.

Yesterday

Words & Music by John Lennon & Paul McCartney

Verse 2:
Suddenly, I'm not half the man I used to be
There's a shadow hanging over me –
Oh, yesterday came suddenly.

Verse 3(𝄋):
Yesterday, love was such an easy game to play
Now I need a place to hide away
Oh, I believe in yesterday.

Your Song

Words & Music by Elton John and Bernie Taupin

Chorus

And you__ can tell ev - 'ry - bod - y this__ is { your / the } song._____

It may__ be quite__ sim - ple but_____ now that it's done,__

____ I hope you don't mind,_____ I hope you don't mind

____ that I put__ down in words how won - der - ful

To Coda ⊕

D.C. *(with repeats)* **al Coda** ⊕

life is__ while you're__ in__ the world.__

⊕ **Coda**

you're__ in_____ the world._____

Verse 2:   If I was a sculptor, but then again no
              Or a man who makes potions in a travelin' show
              I know it's not much but it's the best I can do
              My gift is my song and this one's for you.

Verse 3:   I sat on the roof and I kicked off the moss
              Well a few of the verses, well they've got me quite cross
              But the sun's been quite kind while I wrote this song
              It's for people like you that keep it turned on.

Verse 4:   So excuse me forgetting, but these days I do
              You see I've forgotten if they're green or they're blue
              Anyway, the thing is, what I really mean
              Yours are the sweetest eyes I've ever seen.

Zombie

Words & Music by Dolores O'Riordan

You Oughta Know

Words & Music by Alanis Morissette & Glenn Ballard

Ah.   Ah.   Ah.

(Vocal tacet 1°)

Ah.   Ah.   Ah.

D. %: al Coda

Ah.   Ah.   Ah.   'Cause the

Coda

ought-a know_ why I'm here___ to re-mind___ you of the mess_

___ you left___ when you went a-way. It's not fair____ to de-ny___

___ me of the cross_ I bear_ that you gave to me. You, you, you ought-a know.__

160